Issued under the authority of the Home Office (Fire D...

Manual o

Firemans

A survey of the science of fire-fig... ...g

G000231659

Book 1

Elements of combustion and extinction

London
Her Majesty's Stationery Office

ISBN 0 11 340581 2

Preface

In this, the first Book in this series of the *Manual of Firemanship*, it is appropriate that an attempt is made to explain basic principles of the properties of matter especially in relation to fire and fire extinction. It is necessary that a firefighter has some idea why materials behave in the way they do under various physical and chemical stresses.

However, it is not intended to be either a physics or a chemistry textbook and the contents are confined to those aspects of both disciplines which have a relevance to a firefighter's tasks.

The titles of Parts 1 "The physics of combustion" and 2 "The chemistry of combustion" are sufficiently concise. Part 3 "Extinguishing fires" not only relates the principles of Parts 1 and 2 to fire extinction but also includes classification of fires and briefly touches on some of the media used and methods of extinction.

Metrication

List of SI units for use in the Fire Service

Quantity and basic or derived SI unit and symbol	Approved unit of measurement	Conversion factor
Length metre (m)	kilometre (km) metre (m) millimetre (mm)	1 km = 0.621 mile 1 m = 1.093 yards = 3.279 feet 1 mm = 0.039 inch
Area square metre (m²)	square kilometre (km²) square metre (m²) square millimetre (mm²)	1 km² = 0.386 mile² 1 m² = 1.196 yards² = 10.764 feet² 1 mm² = 0.002 inch²
Volume cubic metre (m³)	cubic metre (m³) litre (l) (= 10⁻³ m³)	1 m³ = 35.7 feet³ 1 litre = 0.22 gallon
Volume, flow cubic metre per second (m³/s)	cubic metre per second (m³/s) litres per minute (l/min)	1 m³/s = 35.7 feet³/s 1 l/min = 0.22 gall/min
Mass kilogram (kg)	kilogram (kg) tonne (t)	1 kg = 2.205 lbs 1 t = 0.984 ton
Velocity metre per second (m/s)	metre per second (m/s) international knot (kn) (= 1.852 km/h) kilometre per hour (km/h)	1 m/s = 3.281 feet/second 1 km/h = 0.621 mile/ hour
Acceleration metre per second²(m/s²)	metre/second² (m/s²)	1 m/s² = 3.281 feet/second² = 0.102 'g'

Quantity and basic or derived SI unit and symbol	Approved unit of measurement	Conversion factor
Force newton (N)	kilonewton (kN) newton (n)	1 kN = 0.1 ton force 1 N = 0.225 lb force
Energy, work joule (J) (= 1 Nm)	joule (J) Kilojoule (kJ) Kilowatt/hour (kW/h)	1 kJ = 0.953 British Thermal Unit 1 J = 0.738 foot lb force
Power watt (W) (= 1 J/s = 1 Nm/s)	kilowatt (kW) watt (W)	1 kW = 1.34 horsepower 1 W = 0.735 foot lb force/second
Pressure newton/metre^2 (N/m^2)	bar (= 10^{5}N/m^2) millibar (mbar) (= 10^{2}N/m^2) metrehead (= 0.0981 bar)	1 bar = 0.991 atmosphere = 14.5 lb force/in^2 1 mbar = 0.0288 inch Hg 1 metrehead = 3.28 foot head
Heat, quantity of heat joule (J)	joule (J) kilojoule (kJ)	1 kJ = 0.953 British Thermal Unit
Heat flow rate watt	watt (W) kilowatt (kW)	1 W = 3.41 British Thermal Units/hour 1 kW = 0.953 British Thermal Unit/second
Specific energy, calorific value, specific latent heat joule/kilogram (J/kg) joule/m^3 (J/m^3)	kilojoule/kilogram (kJ/kg) kilojoule/m^3 (kJ/m^3) megajoule/m^3 (MJ/m^3)	1 kJ/kg = 0.43 British Thermal Unit/lb 1 kJ/m^3 = 0.0268 British Thermal Unit/ft^3
Temperature degree Celsius (°C)	degree Celsius (°C)	1 degree Celsius = 1 degree Centigrade

Contents

Part 1
The physics of combustion

Chapter 1 Physical properties of matter

1 Density, specific gravity and vapour density   1
2 Matter and energy   6
3 Melting point, freezing point and boiling point   8

Chapter 2 Heat and temperature

1 Measurement of temperature   10
2 Thermometric scales—centigrade or Celsius scale,
  Fahrenheit scale   11
3 Conversion of scales   12
4 Other methods of measuring temperature—air or
  gas thermometer, use of solids, thermo-couples,
  electrical resistance, comparison by brightness   13
5 The kelvin absolute scale of temperature   15
6 Heat units—the joule, the calorie, British thermal
  unit   15
7 Specific heat   16
8 Change of state and latent heat—latent heat of
  vaporisation, effect of change of pressure on boiling
  point and latent heat, latent heat of fusion,
  calculation of latent heat, cooling produced by
  evaporation   17

Chapter 3 Thermal expansion

1 Thermal expansion of solids—coefficient of linear expansion, nickel-iron alloy (invar), allowance in large metal structures, thermostats, coefficients of superficial and cubical expansion of solids   20
2 Thermal expansion of liquids—cubical expansion, effect on density   23
3 Expansion of gases—temperature, pressure and volume, the gas laws, Boyle's law, Charles' law, the law of pressures, the general gas laws   24
4 Liquefaction of gases—critical temperature and pressure, liquefied gases in cylinder   26
5 Sublimation   27

Chapter 4 The transmission of heat

1 Conduction   30
2 Convection   30
3 Radiation—transmission, absorption, reflection   32

Part 2
The chemistry of combustion

Chapter 5 The basis of chemistry

1 Atoms and molecules   39
2 Compounds and mixtures   43
3 Symbols—use of symbols in writing formulae, radicals   43
4 Atomic weight   46
5 Molecular weight   47
6 Valency—multiple valency, nomenclature   48
7 Simple equations   50
8 Use of chemical equations   51
9 Limitations of chemical equations—reality, physical state, reaction conditions, heat, heat of reaction   52

Chapter 6 Combustion

1 Factors involved in combustion   54
2 Heat of reaction and calorific value   55
3 The nature of flame   56
4 Ignition temperature—flash point, fire point,
  spontaneous ignition temperature, spontaneous
  combustion   56
5 Limits of flammability   58
6 Hazards of oxidising agents—nitric acid and the
  inorganic nitrates, permanganates, chlorates,
  chromates and dichromates, inorganic peroxides,
  ogranic oxidising agents, organic peroxides and
  hydroperoxides   58

Chapter 7 Combustible organic substances

1 Aliphatic compounds (hydrocarbons: the paraffins)   62
2 Unsaturated hydrocarbons—olefines, acetylenes   66
3 Aromatic hydrocarbons   67
4 Liquefied petroleum gases   71

Chapter 8 Solvents

1 Alcohols   73
2 Aldehydes   73
3 Ketones   74
4 Carboxylic acids   75
5 Esters   76
6 Ethers   78

Chapter 9 Plastics

1 The nature of organic solids polymers   80
2 Production of toxic and corrosive gases   82
3 Fire hazards of plastics—the evolution of large
  quantities of smoke, production of burning tars or
  droplets, exotherms, catalysts, use of flammable
  solvents, dusts, self-extinguishing plastics   83
4 Dangers associated with monomers—acrylonitrile,
  butadiene, epichlorhydrin, methyl methacrylate,
  styrene, vinyl acetate, vinyl chloride   85
5 Intermediates and hardeners—isocyanates,
  chlorosilanes, epoxide resins   86

Chapter 10 Other combustible solids

1 Wood   88
2 Coal   88
3 Metals—properties of metals, reaction of metals with
   water or steam, formation of oxides and combustion   89
4 Sulphur   92
5 Phosphorus   92
The halogens—fluorine, chlorine, bromine, iodine   93

Part 3
Extinguishing fire

Chapter 11 Methods of extinguishing fire

1 Starvation   97
2 Smothering   98
3 Cooling   100

Chapter 12 Fire extinguishing media

 1 Classification of fires by type—Classes 'A', 'B', 'C'
    and 'D'   103
 2 Classification of fires by size   104
 3 Water   104
 4 Steam   105
 5 Foam and foam-making compounds   105
 6 Vaporising liquids   107
 7 Carbon dioxide and inert gases   107
 8 Dry chemical powders   108
 9 Sand, etc.   109
10 Blanketing   109
11 Beating out   109

Part 1
The physics of combustion

In order to understand the phenomena of fire and fire extinction, some knowledge of physical and chemical principles is necessary, including the properties of matter and, in particular, the physical phenomena associated with the heating and cooling of construction materials. This Part deals with the physical properties of matter. The chemical principles are dealt with in Part 2.

Chapter 1
Physical properties of matter

Matter may be defined as something which possesses mass and occupies space. This definition applies not only to solids and liquids, but also to gases and vapours.

1 Density, specific gravity and vapour density

The most familiar properties of matter are those concerning size and weight. Arising from these, it is common knowledge that some substances are heavier than others, bulk for bulk. Wood floats in water—iron sinks. This difference is expressed in terms of density or specific gravity.

a. Density

The density of a substance is its mass per unit volume. Density may be calculated by dividing the mass of a body by the volume:

density is therefore $\dfrac{\text{mass}}{\text{volume}}$

or, expressed in symbols $\quad D = \dfrac{M}{V}$

hence $\qquad\qquad M = D \times V$

and $\qquad\qquad V = \dfrac{M}{D}$

In this country density has been measured in pounds per cubic foot, but under metrication the SI units of density are kilograms per cubic metre (kg/m^3) or grams per cubic centimetre (g/cm^3). Water has a density of $1\ Mg/m^3$ ($1000\ kg/m^3$) or a $1\ g/cm^3$. Mercury has the very high density of $13{\cdot}6\ Mg/m^3$ or $13{\cdot}6\ g/cm^3$ and is therefore $13{\cdot}6$ times as dense as water.

b. Relative density or specific gravity

The relative density of a substance is the ratio of the mass of any volume of it to the mass of an equal volume of water.

Relative density $= \dfrac{\text{mass of any volume of the substance}}{\text{mass of an equal volume of water}}$

It should be noted that relative density or specific gravity has no units; it is simply a number or ratio and it is the same whatever system of units is being used for expressing densities.

c. Vapour density

The density of a gas or vapour (usually abbreviated VD) is often given in relation to the density of an equal volume of hydrogen, air or oxygen under the same conditions of temperature and pressure. If compared with water, this specific gravity would be very small indeed (for example the specific gravity of air as related to water is 0·0013). Hydrogen is often used as a basis of vapour density because it is the lightest gas, and the vapour density of air as compared with hydrogen is 14·4. For carbon dioxide the corresponding figure is 22, and carbon dioxide is, therefore, about $1\frac{1}{2}$ times as heavy as air at the same temperature and pressure. For fire service purposes it is usually much more convenient to compare the density of gases and vapours with that of air, but in that case the reference gas should always be quoted; e.g. the vapour density of methane is 0·556 (air = 1), or the vapour density of methane is 8 (hydrogen = 1).

The following are examples of vapour density as compared with hydrogen:

	Vapour density	
Hydrogen	1)	lighter
Methane	8 }	than
Ammonia	8·5)	air
Air (mainly nitrogen and oxygen)	14·4	
Carbon dioxide	22)	heavier
Sulphur dioxide	32 }	than
Chlorine	35·5)	air

d. Importance of density

Density is of far reaching importance, especially to the fireman. The density or specific gravity of a burning liquid partly determines whether it is possible to cover it with water to extinguish the fire, or whether it will be necessary to use foam or other extinguishing medium. The miscibility of the liquid with water will also be a factor here. It is the density of a gas or vapour which determines whether it will be met in the highest concentrations at the higher or lower level of a building.

If water is poured into two tanks (a) and (b) (Fig. 1.1) connected by a pipe at the base, the liquid will assume the same level in each because the contents have the same density. If, however, the water in one, say (b) is replaced by petrol, the level of the latter will be higher because petrol has a specific gravity of about 0·75. Moreover, if water

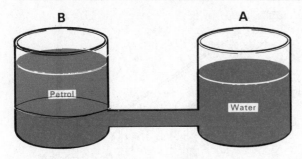

Fig. 1.1 Diagram showing the difference in density of liquids.

is added to tank (a), the water will raise the petrol in (b) and eventually displace it entirely from the tank. The fact that petrol and other flammable liquids float on water must never be overlooked in firemanship, for it may well lead to the spread of conflagration where liquids on fire are involved.

e. Difference in density of gases

The influence of the difference of density in gases is even more important. Gases have a certain parallelism with the behaviour of petrol and water in tanks, which is exemplified by a chimney full of the hot products of combustion. The chimney (Fig. 1.2) may be regarded as a tank full of hot light gas communicating at the base with another tank full of cold gas, i.e. the surrounding outside air. Considering the gases occupying the same height—the height of the chimney—we have, therefore, two volumes of gases of equal height but of different weight, and therefore unbalanced. In order to restore the balance, cold air from outside flows into the base of the chimney and displaces hot gas in the chimney. This would continue until the chimney is full of cold air, but in practice the process is maintained continuously by the fire at the base of the chimney which replaces the hot chimney gas which is driven from the top of the chimney.

If, however, the outflow of hot gas from the chimney is prevented by means of a cover or damper, a pressure will develop at the top of the chimney. The weight of the column of lighter hot gas in the chimney is insufficient to balance the weight of the heavier cold outside air. This unbalanced condition is responsible for a force which is expended in driving gas from the top of an open chimney. When the top is closed the force is found in the form of an equivalent pressure which can be calculated if the densities of the gases are known.

In a burning building, similar conditions are developed. Inside the air is heated, becomes lighter, rises and escapes through any openings which may be available. If ways of escape do not exist, a pressure will

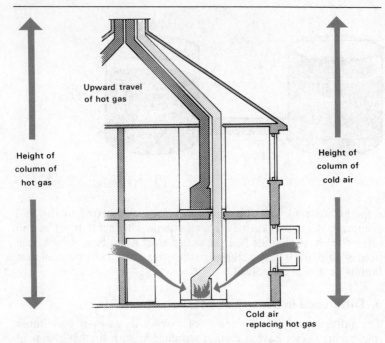

Fig. 1.2 Diagram of a chimney showing the travel of convection currents.

be developed on the walls of the upper parts of the structure. It is easy to see that the opening of a door or window may release this pressure and in so doing cause an outrush of hot gas or flames which may involve any person acting incautiously. The effect of making such an opening is to convert the building into an open chimney, the hot gases escaping above being replaced by cold fresh air from below, which serves to intensify the fire.

f. Effect of density on behaviour of gases

Difference in density may operate in a similar way whenever gases come together. Light gases such as methane (a constituent of natural gas) which has a vapour density of 0·5 approximately compared with air, will rise to a ceiling and only slowly interdiffuse with air afterwards. Heavy gases, such as carbon dioxide (vapour density 1·53 compared with air) and petrol vapours (vapour density 2·5 compared with air) will accumulate in low places such as wells and cellars, so creating dangers of asphyxia as well as of fire or explosion.

2 Matter and energy

Matter is the name give to all material things, and it can exist in three states—solid, liquid or gas. Some forms of matter, e.g. water, may be found quite commonly in all three states, but many substances are, at normal temperatures, found only in one or two of the states. For example steel is solid up to its melting point of 1400°C (the actual melting point varies according to the composition of the steel). Its boiling point is about 3000°C. Carbon dioxide is normally a gas, but under pressure it can be liquefied and if its temperature is lowered sufficiently, it solidifies. Oxygen is normally a gas but it can be liquefied at very low temperatures. All matter is composed of one or more elements, of which there are about 100 (Table 3, page 40).

All matter is made up of extremely small particles called atoms. Until about 50 years ago it was believed that atoms could not be further divided; hence an atom was defined as a basic particle which could not be split into particles of simpler substances. We know now that this is not strictly true as means have been found for splitting atoms or recombining them to form new atoms. The subject of atomic physics is discussed in the *Manual, Part 6C: Section 11*, '*Radioactive materials*'. Atoms can combine to form molecules. Some molecules consist of one or more atoms of the same kind. These are the molecules of the chemical elements. Other molecules consist of two or more atoms of different kinds. These are molecules of chemical compounds and they can, by chemical means, be split into their component elements. This forms the basis of the science of chemistry, which is dealt with in Part 2.

Energy represents the ability to do work and is available to us in a number of different ways—heat, light, electricity, potential energy (the energy of a body due to its position, e.g. water at the top of a waterfall), kinetic energy (energy due to the movement of a body, e.g. water falling to the bottom of a waterfall) (Fig. 1.3).

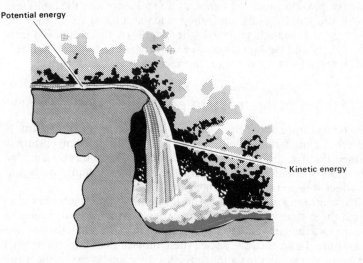

Potential energy

Kinetic energy

Fig. 1.3 Diagram showing potential and kinetic energy.

The form of energy which is of the most immediate consequence to the fireman is heat. Heat may be produced by a chemical change. One way in which this occurs is in combustion. This represents heat produced by a chemical change and we say that chemical energy has been converted into heat energy. Heat may also be produced by converting mechanical energy or kinetic energy, i.e. by friction.

Energy cannot be created or destroyed—it can only be converted into another form of energy. Strictly speaking, in certain atomic processes, mass can be converted into energy, but this need not concern us at this stage.

The molecules of a substance are in a continual state of motion. This is true even of the molecules of a solid. At the same time, molecules exert a force of attraction to each other, which is greater the nearer they are together. As a result, the kinetic energy of the molecules due to their movement tends to drive them apart while the attractive force, or force of cohesion, tends to bind them together. The lower the temperature, the less kinetic energy the molecules have, and therefore the more sluggish their movement. Below a certain temperature, therefore, the molecules of a substance may be held closely together by the force of cohesion, although the molecules are in fact still vibrating. The substance is then a solid. If heat is applied to a solid, this additional energy is stored in the substance by an increase of the kinetic energy of the molecules, which vibrate faster and tend to force each other apart. The temperature of the body rises and it expands. A point is reached when the molecules are moving fast enough to break free of the cohesive forces to some extent and they become free to roll over each other although they do not have complete freedom. At this point the solid melts and becomes a liquid. Further heating raises the temperature still more and the molecules move still more rapidly, until they reach a point at which they are moving fast enough to break the bonds of the cohesive forces completely and the liquid boils, i.e. it turns into a vapour. If heat is taken away from a substance, the reverse processes occur.

3 Melting point, freezing point and boiling point

The temperature at which a solid melts is called the melting point. If we are dealing with a liquid turning into a solid, the temperature is named the freezing point. These two temperatures are the same for the same substance. The temperature at which a liquid boils and becomes a vapour is the boiling point.

Even at temperatures below boiling point, some molecules may reach the surface of the liquid with enough energy to enable them to escape into the surrounding space as vapour. The liquid is then said to evaporate. In an enclosed space, these molecules of vapour set up a pressure known as the vapour pressure. For any given temperature below the boiling point there is a definite vapour pressure at which the number of molecules which escape are just balanced by the number which are recaptured by the liquid. Boiling occurs when the vapour pressure becomes equal to the surrounding pressure. Vapour then forms not only at the surface of the liquid, but also in the body of the liquid. If the external pressure is increased, the vapour pressure at which boiling will take place is increased and so the temperature must increase. If the external pressure falls, the reverse is true and the temperature at which boiling occurs will be lower.

Since energy is required to overcome the forces of cohesion when a substance melts or boils, the heat which is supplied during these processes does not cause a rise in temperature of the substance. Conversely, when a vapour condenses or a liquid solidifies, it gives up heat without any fall in temperature so long as the change is taking place.

Chapter 2
Heat and temperature

In Chapter 1 energy was defined as the ability to do work, and it was stated that it can neither be created nor destroyed, but can exist in a number of different forms, of which heat is one. Heat may be produced by chemical means, e.g. the burning of coal or oil, or by mechanical means, e.g. by friction. The passage of an electric current through a resistance also produces heat. Heat in its turn may be converted into other forms of energy, e.g. pressure energy in a steam boiler. It is also possible to convert heat back into chemical energy or electrical energy.

Heat energy cannot be measured directly. The most obvious effect of supplying heat energy to a substance is a change of temperature, but temperature is a measure of the hotness of a body, not the amount of heat in it. Heat always flows from high temperature to low temperature. If two bodies, one hot and the other cold, are placed in contact, the hot body (i.e. the one at the higher temperature) loses heat and the cold body (the one at the lower temperature) gains heat.

The fact that heat and temperature are not the same thing can be seen from a simple experiment. A piece of fine iron or copper wire held in the flame of a match will rapidly become red hot and capable of inflicting a burn. A similar match allowed to burn under a kettle containing a pint of water would produce no noticeable change in the temperature of the water because of the greater mass—yet the amount of heat given out by each of the two matches would be about the same.

1 Measurement of temperature

The human body cannot be relied upon to measure temperature. Firstly, it compares the hotness of a substance with some immediately preceding sensation. If one hand is placed in a bowl of cold water and the other in a bowl of hot water, and then after an interval both hands are placed in a bowl of tepid water, the hand which was in the bowl of cold water will feel that the tepid water is 'hot', while that from the hot water will feel that the tepid water is 'cold'. Secondly the human body is unable to give a numerical value to temperature.

Temperature can, however, be measured by making use of one of the effects of heat. The commonest example is the use of the property of thermal expansion of a liquid. The instrument used is known as a thermometer (Fig. 2.1). It consists of a small bulb with a stem with a fine bore, sealed at the end and containing a suitable liquid. The liquid is generally mercury, which has the advantages of a high boiling point (357°C), a uniform expansion and a low heat capacity; it is also opaque. Its freezing point, however, is about –39°C and hence it is not suitable for measuring temperatures greatly below the freezing point of water. Alcohol has a lower freezing point (–112°C) but also a much lower boiling point (78°C) than mercury, and is used for low temperatures. Coloured water is sometimes used for rough work for temperatures between the freezing point and boiling point of water.

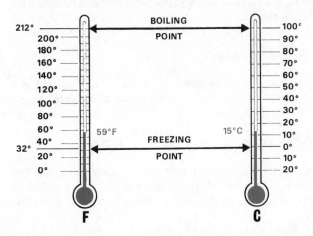

Fig. 2.1 Diagram showing a comparison between the centigrade and Fahrenheit thermometer scales.

2 Thermometric scales

Before constructing a thermometric scale, two fixed points are required. When thermometers were first made, a variety of fixed points were taken (e.g. Fahrenheit's freezing mixture which gave him a temperature 32°F below the freezing point of pure water). Today, the melting point of pure ice and the boiling point, under a pressure of 76 centimetres of mercury, of pure water, are taken as the fixed points. Thus, to determine the lower fixed point of a thermometer, its bulb is placed in melting ice and to determine the upper fixed point the thermometer is placed in steam from water boiling at the standard atmospheric pressure of 76 centimetres of mercury. If the barometric pressure is not 76 centimetres, a correction has to be applied to the upper fixed point. The level at which the liquid in the thermometer stands at each of the fixed points is marked on the stem of the thermometer. Two thermometric scales are in common use.

a. Centigrade or Celsius scale

On this scale the lower fixed point is marked 0. The upper fixed point is marked 100. The stem between these two points is divided into 100 equal division or degrees. These divisions are called centigrade degrees.

b. The Fahrenheit scale*

Because the inventor of this scale used a freezing mixture to give him his lower fixed point, the freezing point of water is 32°F. The upper fixed point is 212°F, and the stem between these marks is divided into 180 Fahrenheit degrees.

3 Conversion of scales

If both scales are marked on the same thermometer, the same length between the fixed points is divided into 100 centigrade degrees or 180 Fahrenheit degrees. Therefore:

$$100 \text{ centigrade degrees} = \frac{180}{100} \text{ divisions} = \frac{9}{5} \text{ divisions}$$

on the Fahrenheit scale. For example, if the temperature on the centigrade scale was 15°C (which means that it is 15 C divisions above the lower fixed point), the reading on the Fahrenheit scale would be

$$15 \times \frac{9}{5} = 27 \text{ Fahrenheit divisions above the lower fixed point.}$$

But the lower fixed point on the Fahrenheit scale is marked 32. So 15°C is equivalent to a Fahrenheit temperature of $27 + 32 = 59$°F.

To convert degrees centigrade to Fahrenheit

Multiply degrees centigrade by $\frac{9}{5}$ and add 32.

i.e. $°F = \left(°C \times \frac{9}{5} \right) + 32.$

To convert degrees Fahrenheit to centigrade

Subtract 32 and then multiply by $\frac{5}{9}$

i.e. $°C = (°F - 32) \times \frac{5}{9}$

---

*With the introduction of metrication, the use of the Fahrenheit scale is being discontinued, and only the centigrade or Celsius scale will be used.

Examples

(A) To convert 80°C to °F

$$\left(80 \times \frac{9}{5}\right) + 32 = (16 \times 9) + 32 = 176°F$$

(B) To convert 167°F to °C

$$(167 - 32) \times \frac{5}{9} = 135 \times \frac{5}{9} \times 75°C$$

For another example let us convert –40°F to the centigrade scale.

–40°F is (40 + 32) = 72°F below freezing

$$C = (F - 32) \frac{5}{9} = (-40 - 32) \frac{5}{9} = -72 \times \frac{5}{9} = -40°C$$

so –40° is the same temperature on both scales.

This gives an alternative method of converting from one scale to the other by using –40 as a new zero point. The method is:

To the temperature on either scale, add 40. Multiply the result by ⁵⁄₉ if converting from Fahrenheit to centigrade or by ⁹⁄₅ if converting from centigrade to Fahrenheit. Then subtract 40.

(C) To convert 15°C to °F

$$15 + 40 = 55 \qquad 55 \times \frac{9}{5} = 99 \qquad 99 - 40 = 59°F$$

(D) To convert 95°F to °C

$$95 + 40 = 135 \qquad 135 \times \frac{5}{5} = 75 \qquad 75 - 40 = 35°C$$

4 Other methods of measuring temperature

The liquid-in-glass thermometer is not the only method of measuring temperature. There are several other methods, such as the following:

a. Air or gas thermometer

Instead of using a liquid, a bulb containing air or some other gas may be used. In one such thermometer, the expansion of the gas causes a short thread of mercury to move along a scale. These thermometers are very sensitive, but may require correction to compensate for atmospheric pressure.

b. Use of solids

The expansion of a solid may be used for temperature measurement. The expansion may be used directly, or the differing expansion of two dissimilar metals may be used.

c. Thermo-couples

When the junction of wires of two different metals (e.g. iron and copper) is heated, an electrical potential is generated. If the wires are connected to a sensitive instrument for detecting electric current, the instrument (Fig. 2.2) will record a current. This current depends on the temperature of the junction. Thermo-couples of this type for

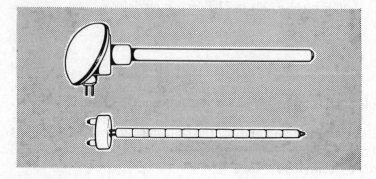

Fig. 2.2 Sketch of a pyrometer of the thermo-couple type. The heat sensitive bi-metallic element (below) is housed in a container (above) which protects it from the effects of heat and mechanical wear and tear.

measuring temperature are known as pyrometers. To increase the sensitivity, several junctions or thermo-couples may be joined in series. Pyrometers are able to record extremely high temperatures.

d. Electrical resistance

The electrical resistance of a wire increases with a rise in temperature and the change of resistance may be used to measure temperature.

e. Comparison by brightness

Temperatures above about 1250°C (e.g. of furnaces) may be measured by comparing the brightness of the object, which at that temperature will be glowing, with that of the filament of an electric lamp whose brightness can be altered by varying the current flowing through it. If the current is too small the filament appears darker than the object but if it is too large the filament appears brighter. When the filament disappears, the corresponding value of the current is a measure of the temperature of the object.

5 The kelvin absolute scale of temperature

A further temperature scale which is important in calculations concerning gases is the *absolute scale*. If a graph of volume and temperature of a gas is drawn, and the graph is produced backwards (Fig. 2.3) to cut the temperature axis where the volume is 0, this temperature will be found to be –273°C. This is the temperature at which the volume of the gas would have contracted to 0 if it had remained a gas. It is regarded as the lowest attainable temperature, and is used as the zero for the *absolute* scales of temperature. There

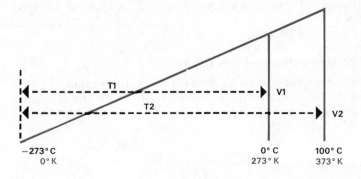

Fig. 2.3 Graph showing the zero on the kelvin or absolute scale.

are two of these—the kelvin scale (named after Sir William Thomson, Lord Kelvin) which uses units which are the same size as the degrees on the centigrade scale, and the Rankine scale, related to the Fahrenheit scale.

Zero on the kelvin scale is –273°C. Hence 0°C is 273 K; 100°C is 373 K and so on. In general, K = °C + 273. (On the Rankine scale 0 is –460°F.) The symbol T is always used for absolute temperature, and the symbol t denotes temperatures other than absolute.

6 Heat units

a. The joule

The SI unit of heat is the *joule*. This is an energy unit which is used for all forms of energy—heat, mechanical energy, electrical energy and so forth. It is defined from mechanics; where energy is the capacity to perform work, and work and energy are measured in the same units, namely joules (J). Work is said to be done when the point of application of a force moves, and we can say:

work done = force × distance moved in direction of the force.

15

The joule is the work done when the application of a force of 1 newton (N) moves through 1 metre in the direction of the force. Larger units are:

the kilojoule (1 kJ = 1000 J)
the megajoule (1 MJ = 1000 kJ)

There are certain older units which have now been replaced by the joule, namely:

b. The calorie

This is defined as the quantity of heat required to raise the temperature of 1 gram of water through 1°C. A kilocalorie = 1000 calories.

1 calorie = 4·18 joules.

c. The British thermal unit (BTu)

This is the quantity of heat required to raise the temperature of 1 lb of water through 1°F. Another British unit is the therm, which is equal to 100 000 BTu (10^5 BTu).

1 BTu = 1·005 kJ

7 Specific heat

Heat energy can be transferred from a place at a higher temperature to one at a lower temperature. As this is an energy transfer, the units used are joules. When heat is added to a body the temperature rises; we may speak of the *heat capacity* of a body as the heat required to raise its temperature by 1°C. The SI unit of heat capacity is therefore the joule per degree C (J/°C). If we take equal masses of water and oil and supply heat to each at the same rate, it is found that the temperature of the oil may rise by 10°C in 3 minutes, but the temperature of the water only rises by 5°C in the same time. Since the rate of supply of heat is the same in both cases, it is clear that oil has a smaller capacity than an equal mass of water.

To compare one substance with another we use specific heat capacity. *Specific heat capacity* of a substance is the heat energy required to raise the temperature of unit mass of it through 1°C. In the SI system we use the unit of joules per kilogram per °C (J/kg per °C). In the following list of specific heat capacities, it will be seen that water has the unusually high specific heat capacity of 4200 J/kg (4·2 kJ/kg) per °C. Very few substances have a higher value than this, the most notable being hydrogen at constant volume, and mixtures of certain alcohols with water.

Some values of specific heat capacities are shown in Table 1.

Materials with a low specific heat capacity will heat up more rapidly in a fire situation than those of high specific heat capacity.

Table 1

Specific heat capacities (joules per kilogram)

	Per degree centigrade
Water	4200
Iron	460
Aluminium	900
Copper	400
Mercury	140
Glass (ordinary)	670
Ice	2100
Earth, rock, etc.	840
Carbon tetrachloride	850
Methylated spirit	2400
Benzene	1720
Glycerol	2560

Substances such as petrol, alcohol and the like have low specific heat capacities and are also readily vaporised; they may also emit dangerous vapours (see Part 2). Low specific heat capacities are of considerable importance in promoting fire risks.

8 Change of state and latent heat

a. Latent heat of vaporisation

When a kettle is put on to boil the temperature of the water rises until it reaches 100°C. At this temperature the water boils, that is to say bubbles of vapour form at the bottom and rise to the surface where they burst and escape as steam. Once the water has started to boil, the temperature remains constant at 100°C. At the same time heat energy is being steadily absorbed from the source of heat (gas flame or heating element). This heat, which is going into the water but not increasing its temperature, is the energy needed to convert the water from the liquid state to the vapour state. Experiments show that 2 260 000 joules are required to convert 1 kilogram of water at its boiling point into steam at the same temperature. This is known as the specific latent heat of steam (latent means hidden). This extra heat goes into the vapour, but does not indicate its presence by producing a rise in temperature.

When the steam condenses to form water the same amount of latent heat is given out again; it is for this reason that certain types of steam engine must be water cooled. Other liquids besides water absorb latent heat when they are turned into vapour. For example 860 000 J are required to convert 1 kg of alcohol into vapour at the same temperature.

The definition, therefore, of the specific latent heat of vaporisation of a substance is the quantity of heat required to change unit mass of the substance from the liquid to the vapour state without change of temperature.

The SI unit of latent heat is the joule per kilogram (J/kg). It is usually expressed in kilojoules per kilogram (kJ/kg).

b. Effect of change of pressure on boiling point and latent heat

Water boils at 100°C when the external pressure is the standard atmospheric pressure of 760 mm of mercury or 1·013 bar (1 bar = 10^5 N/m²). If the external pressure is raised the boiling point is raised, and if the external pressure is lowered, the boiling point is lowered. This is made use of in pressure cookers and in pressurised cooling systems for internal combustion engines, where the increased pressure raises the boiling point of the liquid in the system.

The effect of raising the boiling point is to increase the quantity of heat required to raise the temperature of the cold liquid to the new boiling point and also to decrease the latent heat of vaporisation.

c. Latent heat of fusion

Just as latent heat is taken in when water changes to vapour at the same temperature, a similar thing happens when ice melts to form water. In this case, the latent heat is not so great. It requires 336 000 J to convert 1 kg of ice at 0°C to water at the same temperature. Likewise, when water at 0°C freezes into ice, the same quantity of heat is given out for every 1 kg of ice formed. This is called the specific latent heat of fusion of ice. This is not confined to water alone; other substances absorb latent heat when they melt and conversely they give out latent heat on solidifying. This is the latent heat of fusion.

The definition of the specific latent heat of fusion of a substance is the quantity of heat required to convert unit mass of the substance from the solid to the liquid state without change in temperature. The same units (J/kg or kJ/kg, etc.) are used as for the latent heat of vaporisation.

d. Calculation of latent heat

To find the quantity of heat required to completely convert 2 g of ice at −6°C to steam at 100°C at standard atmospheric pressure, one requires to know:

Specific heat capacity of ice   2·1 kJ/kg   (= 2·1 J/g)   per °C

Specific heat capacity of water   4·2 kJ/kg   (= 4·2 J/g)   per °C

Specific latent heat of ice   336 kJ/kg (= 336 J/g) per °C

Specific latent heat of steam   2260 kJ/kg (=2260 J/g) per °C

The quantity of heat is then found as follows:

(i)   Quantity of heat required to raise temperature of
      2 g of ice from –6°C to 0°C = 2 × 2·1 × 6   =   25·2 J

(ii) Quantity of heat required to melt 2 g of ice at 0°C
      = 2 × 336   =   672   J

(iii) Quantity of heat required to raise 2 g of water
      from 0°C to 100°C = 2 × 4·2 × 100   =   840   J

(iv) Quantity of heat required to vaporise 2 g of water
      at 100°C = 2 × 2260

                                                     =   4520 J

                                    Total = 6057·2 J

It will therefore require 6057·2 joules of heat to convert 2 g of ice at –6°C to steam at 100°C.

e. Cooling produced by evaporation

Some liquids have a low boiling point and thus change from liquid to vapour quite easily at ordinary temperatures. Methylated spirit and ether are of this type and are called volatile liquids. If a little methylated spirit or ether is dropped on the hand, it evaporates rapidly and the hand feels very cold. Some local anaesthetics work in this way. To change from liquid to vapour, the liquid absorbs latent heat from the hand, which therefore feels cold. Water would also cause the hand to become cold but not so noticeably as methylated spirit. The spirit has a lower boiling point than water and so it evaporates more quickly at the temperature of the hand.

Chapter 3
Thermal expansion

1 Thermal expansion of solids

In general a substance (solid, liquid or gas) expands when heated, unless it is prevented from doing so by some external agency, by a change of state or by a change in chemical composition.

When a solid is heated, it expands in all three dimensions and therefore increases in length, breadth and thickness. Frequently the increase in length is the most important and the determination of expansion in area and volume follows from it. It is found that within normal ranges of temperature, solids which are homogeneous (i.e. uniform) in structure, expand uniformly, i.e. the expansion of a bar is proportional to the rise in temperature. The expansion is also proportional to the length of the bar, but varies with the nature of the substance of which the bar is made.

a. Coefficient of linear expansion

The amount by which unit length of a substance expands when its temperature is raised by one degree is called the *coefficient of linear expansion* of the substance. The temperature scale must be stated. Thus we can say that the coefficient of linear expansion of a solid is the increase in length of unit length when its temperature is raised by one degree. From this we can calculate the increase in length of a body from the expression:

$$\text{Increase in length} = \text{original length} \times \text{coefficient of linear expansion} \times \text{rise in temperature}$$

This gives the increase in length, so that to find the new length, the original length must be added.

For steel the coefficient of linear expansion is 0·000012 per °C. Thus, a bar of steel 1 metre long expands by 0·000012 m for each °C rise in temperature, a 1 km bar expands by 0·000012 km for each °C rise in temperature, and so on.

Some other typical values of the coefficient of linear expansion are:

Aluminium	0·000023 per °C
Copper	0·000017 per °C
Concrete	0·000012 per °C
Common glass	0·000009 per °C
Pyrex glass	0·000003 per °C

b. Nickel-iron alloy (invar)

There is an iron alloy containing 36 per cent nickel (i.e. 64% iron, 36% nickel) which has a coefficient of linear expansion of 0·0000001 per °C—i.e. less than 1 per cent of that of steel. This is so small as to be negligible in most cases. This alloy is called *invar* and is used for the manufacture of measuring rods and tapes which are required to be accurate over a range of temperature. It can also be used for the manufacture of watch and clock parts or parts of other mechanisms which must remain unchanged in size over a range of temperature. It should be noted that this very small coefficient of expansion applies only to that particular nickel-iron alloy which contains 36 per cent of nickel.

c. Allowance in large metal structures

In large metal structures which are subjected to large variations in temperature, allowance must be made for the linear expansion of the parts. In large bridges, this allowance may be quite large itself. For instance, the Forth road bridge has a total length of about 1960 metres. The range of temperature between winter and summer may well be between –30°C and +30°C. The difference between the maximum and minimum lengths of the roadway would be:

$$1960 \times 60 \times 0 \cdot 000012 = 1 \cdot 41 \text{ metres}$$

Even a bridge with a span of 20 metres could change by 14 mm between the hottest and coldest temperatures. Allowance for this expansion is often made by fixing one end of the bridge and resting the other on rollers, or on a sliding bearing, so that the bridge may expand and contract without exerting a side load on its piers. Railway lines used to be laid in 13·7 or 18·3 m lengths, with gaps to allow for expansion and contraction, but modern methods now make it possible for the expansion to be taken up as a tension or compression in the rail, with expansion joints at distances of about 0·8 km.

In buildings, the normal range of temperature may not be so great, since internal heating may keep up the minimum temperature and the structure may protect steelwork from excessive outside heat. However, some allowance must be made for expansion to prevent steelwork from distorting the walls of the building, even if the allowance is only in the form of a clearance between steelwork and brickwork. In a fire situation, however, the increase in temperature may be very great and the situation could arise in which a long beam could exert sufficient side load on a wall and cause it to collapse.

The heat on the inner side of the wall of a burning building, particularly if it is made of a poor conductor, may cause it to expand at a higher rate than the outer side, thus causing the wall to lean outwards and some cases collapse.

d. Thermostats

If two strips of different metals equal in length are laid side by side and their temperatures increased, each will increase in length according to its own coefficient of linear expansion. If two strips of different metals are fastened together throughout their length, thereby preventing them from moving independently, a change of temperature will cause them to become distorted in shape, and to curve, forming the arc of a circle. Such a strip is known as a bi-metallic strip (Fig. 3.1, *left*). If one end of a bi-metallic strip is fixed, a variation of temperature will cause the other end to move. The movement of this free end can be made to close an electric circuit, e.g. to cause an alarm to be operated, or conversely it may be designed to open an electric circuit and switch off a heating appliance. Such a piece of apparatus is known as a thermostat. Alternatively, a rod of one metal inside a tube of another metal (Fig. 3.1, *right*) may be used. One end of the tube is fixed and the rod is fixed to the other end of the tube.

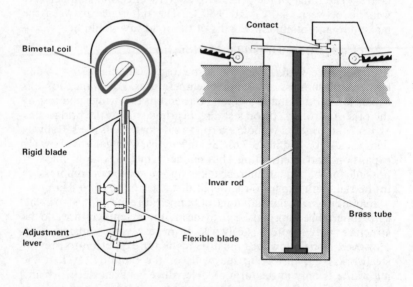

Fig. 3.1 Two types of thermostat. Left: a bi-metallic strip used to make an electrical contact when heat is applied. Right: an alternative type with a rod of one metal inside a tube of another metal.

In some devices of this latter type, the rod is of invar and the tube of brass. In the thermostat shown in Fig. 3.1, right, this combination would result in the contact being broken as the temperature rose above a previously set value.

e. Coefficients of superficial and cubical expansion of solids

It can be shown mathematically that the coefficient of superficial (or area) expansion of a solid is twice the linear coefficient, and that of cubical expansion is three times the linear coefficient. These values depend on the external dimensions of the solid and are not affected by any voids. The cubical expansion of a hollow metal box is the same as that of a solid block of the same metal of the same volume as the box.

2 Thermal expansion of liquids

a. Cubical expansion

Since liquids have no shape and therefore no fixed dimensions other than volume, the only expansion which can be measured is that of cubical expansion. Since a liquid has to be contained in a vessel, the apparent expansion of the liquid is affected by the expansion of the vessel, and the apparent expansion is therefore always less than the real expansion. However, the coefficient of cubical expansion of liquids is considerably greater than that of solids so (with the exception of water, which is dealt with below) the expansion of a liquid is always greater than that of its container.

The coefficient of cubical expansion of glass, for example, is $0.000024/°C$ (i.e. 0.000008×3). That of mercury is $0.00019/°C$ and that of alcohol is $0.00011/°C$. So the thermal expansion of mercury is about $7\frac{1}{2}$ times that of glass, while that of alcohol is nearly 50 times that of glass. Since the coefficient of cubical expansion of steel is $0.000036/°C$, and that of many liquids is of the order of $0.001/°C$, i.e. 30 times as much, it follows that a sealed container of liquid may be a hazard in a fire situation because of the internal pressure which may be set up, unless there is an air space or relief valve to reduce the pressure.

b. Effect on density

Since the density of a substance is the ratio of its mass to its volume, an increase of temperature results in a decrease of density; or conversely, the volume of a given mass of the substance increases as its temperature rises.

Water behaves in a peculiar way. Its expansion is not uniform, the expansion between 30°C and 50°C being double that between 10°C and 30°C. On cooling below 10°C, water contracts until its temperature reaches 4°C. On further cooling it expands until its volume at 0°C is 0.00012 times greater than its volume at 4°C. It also expands further when it freezes. This means that water in ponds and lakes freezes from the top downward and, once the temperature on the surface has fallen to 4°C, further cooling of the lower level can only occur by conduction and is slow because water is a poor conductor.

3 Expansion of gases

a. Temperature, pressure and volume

Since a gas expands to fill all the available space, the volume of a gas may be changed by altering the volume of its container. If the volume is decreased, the pressure is increased. This can be explained by saying that the same number of molecules of the gas occupy a smaller space and therefore collide with each other and with the container walls more frequently. The pressure is due to these collisions—more collisions, more pressure. Heating a gas increases the kinetic energy of the molecules, which therefore move faster, and again collide more frequently. Hence heating a gas increases its pressure—provided its volume is unchanged. By increasing its volume as it is heated, the pressure can be kept constant.

There are, therefore, three variables when dealing with a gas: temperature, pressure and volume, whereas in dealing with a solid or a liquid, temperature and volume are important, pressure is negligible.

b. The gas laws

Solids and liquids have their own expansion rates with rise in temperature, but all gases expand by the same amount for the same temperature rise. When considering the changes in volume of a gas, it must be borne in mind that this is affected by temperature and pressure. In practice these two often happen simultaneously, but to study the effect of either, the other must be maintained at its constant value.

(1) Boyle's Law

The change in volume of a gas by pressure alone is the subject of one of the 'gas laws', known as *Boyle's Law*, which states that:

> 'The volume of a gas is inversely proportional to the pressure upon it provided the temperature is constant.'

Experiments show that if the pressure applied to a given mass of gas is doubled, the volume of the gas is halved. If the pressure is trebled, the volume is reduced to one-third, provided the temperature is constant.

If we have a cylinder whose capacity is 1 cubic metre (1 m³) it can contain 1 m³ of a gas at 1 atmosphere (approximately 1 bar), but if 120 m³ of gas are pumped into the same cylinder the pressure will be 120 atmospheres. If half of the gas is allowed to escape, then the pressure will fall to 60 atmospheres. From this it will be seen that the pressure gauge on a set of breathing apparatus indicates the amount of oxygen in the cylinder. In practice, when a gas is being compressed, e.g. the charging of a breathing apparatus cylinder, or the inflation of a motor car tyre, heat is generated causing an increase in temperature, but this increase is only for the duration of the pumping operation. If the pressure of the gas is measured before the temperature has returned to its original level, it will not be in accordance with Boyle's Law, since the temperature is not the same as it was before the pumping commenced.

Mathematically, if V_1 and P_1 are the initial volume and pressure, and V_2 and P_2 are the final volumes and pressure, then

$$\frac{V_2}{V_1} = \frac{P_1}{P_2} \qquad P_1 V_1 = P_2 V_2$$

or Initial pressure $\times$ Initial volume = Final pressure $\times$ Final volume.

(2) Charles' Law

Experiments show that all gases expand by $\frac{1}{273}$ of their volume at $0°C$ for each $1°C$ rise in temperature, provided that they are maintained at constant pressure. Since the expansion for each $1°C$ rise in temperature is quite large, it is essential to take the initial volume at $0°C$. These experiments were carried out by a French scientist named Charles at the beginning of the 19th century, and the law named after him states:

'The volume of a given mass of gas increases by $\frac{1}{273}$ of its volume at $0°C$ for every $1°C$ rise in temperature provided the pressure upon it remains constant.'

It will be seen from the graph shown in Fig. 2.3 (page 15) of the volume and temperature of a gas that the temperature scale is the Absolute scale, and that the relationship between volume and temperature is:

$$\frac{V_1}{T_1} = \frac{V_2}{T_2}$$

where V_1 and T_1 are the initial volume and absolute temperature and V_2 and T_2 are the final volume and absolute temperature ($°C$). In other words, the volume of a given mass of gas is directly proportional to its absolute temperature, provided that its pressure is kept constant.

(3) The Law of Pressures

There is a third law which can be deduced from the previous two. This concerns the relationship between the pressure and temperature of a gas when the volume is kept constant. Such conditions exist when a cylinder of gas, whose valve is closed, undergoes a rise of temperature, as it does when involved in a fire. This is expressed mathematically as:

$$\frac{P_1}{T_1} = \frac{P_2}{T_2}$$

i.e. the pressure of a given mass of gas is directly proportional to its absolute temperature, provided its volume is kept constant.

(4) The general gas law

The three gas laws can be combined into a single expression:

$$\frac{P_1 V_1}{T_1} = \frac{P_2 V_2}{T_2}$$

This may be used when pressure, temperature and volume all change. It may also be used as a convenient method of remembering the three individual laws, since each of these can be obtained by striking out of the general law the quantity which is being kept constant.

It is important to remember that these gas laws are applicable to all gases provided that they remain as gases over the temperature and pressure range involved. When the temperature and pressure levels at which liquefaction occurs are approached, the gas laws no longer apply.

4 Liquefaction of gases

It has been stated that an increase in pressure raises the boiling point of a liquid. Many substances which are gases at atmospheric temperature and pressure can be compressed to such an extent that their boiling point is raised above atmospheric temperature and the gas liquefies. Other gases cannot be liquefied at atmospheric temperature no matter how great a pressure is applied. These are the so-called 'permanent gases'. However, if the temperature is lowered sufficiently, they can be liquefied by pressure.

a. Critical temperature and pressure

There is, therefore, a *critical temperature* above which a gas cannot be liquefied by increase of pressure alone. For example, a carbon dioxide compressed at 20°C will liquefy. But at 40°C it remains a gas. Its critical temperature is in fact 31·1°C. Below this temperature it can be liquefied by increased pressure and it should properly be described as a vapour. Above this temperature it cannot be liquefied and is properly described as a gas.

The pressure required to liquefy a vapour at its critical temperature is called the *critical pressure*.

Some typical values of critical temperatures and critical pressures are shown in Table 2.

b. Liquefied gases in cylinders

Liquefied gases in cylinders do not obey the gas laws, since any change in temperature, pressure or volume will result in either the liquefaction of gas or the evaporation of liquid provided that the critical temperature is not exceeded. Thus the pressure in a cylinder of liquefied gas will remain constant as gas is drawn off (provided the temperature remains constant) since more liquid will evaporate to make up for the gas drawn off until all the liquid is evaporated. The pressure in the cylinder is not therefore any indication of the amount of gas in the cylinder.

Table 2

	Critical temperature	Critical pressure	
	Degrees C	bars	lbf/in^2
Water (steam)	374	—	—
Sulphur dioxide	157	219	3200
Chlorine	144	78	1140
Ammonia	132	77·7	1120
Nitrous oxide	39	—	—
Carbon dioxide	31·1	73·1	1070
Oxygen	−119	50	730
Nitrogen	−147	33·7	493
Hydrogen	−240	12·9	188

A true gas (i.e. one at a temperature above its critical temperature) will, however, obey the gas laws and the pressure will fall as gas is drawn off. Thus the pressure in the cylinder is an indication of the quantity of gas it contains.

Wnen liquefied gases are stored in cylinders, allowance must be made for expansion of the liquid and its possible ultimate conversion into vapour if it is heated. If the temperature rises above the critical temperature the pressure will rise, possibly to a dangerous level, with a risk of explosion. To minimise this danger, cylinders are never completely filled with liquid.

The weight of a liquefied gas which may be charged into a cylinder is determined by its filling ratio, which varies from gas to gas and depends, among other things, on the density of the liquid.

Filling ratio: $\dfrac{\text{Weight of liquefied gas which may be charged}}{\text{Weight of water which completely fills the cylinder}}$

The filling ratio for ammonia is 0·5, so that a cylinder capable of holding 10 kg of water may only be charged with 5 kg of ammonia. A cylinder of the same size could be charged with 12·5 kg of sulphur dioxide, for which the filling ratio is 1·25.

5 Sublimation

In the laboratory it is possible to produce such low pressures that the boiling point of water can be reduced to 0°C and lower. When this happens ice cannot be melted into water, but vaporises completely on a rise in temperature. Such a change of state from solid to gas cannot be termed either melting or boiling and is given the special name of *sublimation*. In order to achieve sublimation with water, extremely low pressures are required, but carbon dioxide sublimes at atmospheric pressure.

An *increase* in pressure on carbon dioxide will restore the normal sequence of melting followed at a higher temperature by boiling, so that under pressure (and only under pressure) is it possible to have liquid carbon dioxide.

Chapter 4
The transmission of heat

Heat travels from regions of high temperature to regions of lower temperature. This is true no matter how small the temperature difference. There are three methods (Fig. 4.1) by which heat may be transmitted:

(a) conduction;

(b) convection;

(c) radiation.

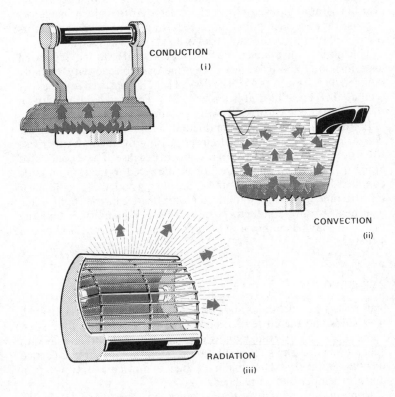

CONDUCTION
(i)

CONVECTION
(ii)

RADIATION
(iii)

Fig. 4.1 Diagram showing how heat is transmitted:
(i) conduction; (ii) convection; (iii) radiation.

1 Conduction

Conduction may occur in solids, liquids or gases, although it is most clearly present in solids. In conduction, heat energy is passed on from one molecule to the next, much as water is passed from one man to the next in a bucket chain. In the bucket chain the men only move a very small distance to either side of their mean position—it is only the water which passes on. In conduction of heat, the molecules vibrate about a mean position and pass on heat energy by colliding with their neighbours.

The ability to conduct heat (thermal conductivity) varies between materials. Most metals conduct heat relatively easily, and are therefore classed as good conductors, though their abilities to conduct heat vary among themselves. The best conductors of heat are silver and copper. Aluminium has about half the thermal conductivity of silver and iron about one-eighth. Non-metallic solids are poor conductors and all liquids (except mercury, which is a metal) and gases are very poor conductors of heat. In fact, some solids and also liquids and gases, are sometimes referred to as heat insulators because they are such poor conductors. In general good conductors of electricity are good conductors of heat, and vice-versa.

The ability of a material to conduct heat can be measured experimentally and is known as the 'thermal conductivity' (usually denoted by K) (see page 15). The flow of heat is measured in joules per second (J/s) and this unit is the watt (W). Thermal conductivity on the SI system is measured in watts per metre per °C (W/m K.)

In fire situations, thermal conductivity is important in terms of the danger of fire spread. A steel girder passing through an otherwise fireproof wall may be a cause of fire spread because of heat conducted along it (Fig. 4.2). A plain steel door subjected to heat on one side conducts heat rapidly to the other side, but a wooden door (though it may become ignited) is, initially, a more effective barrier to heat due to it being a poor conductor. The relative conductivity of building materials may be an important factor in the fire-resisting ability of a structure.

2 Convection

This occurs only in liquids and gases. When a liquid or a gas is heated, it expands and therefore becomes less dense. The lighter fluid rises, being displaced by colder and therefore denser fluid. This in turn becomes heated and so a circulation is set up. Heat energy is carried throughout the fluid by actual movement of molecules until a state of uniform temperature is reached.

Convection is used in domestic hot water systems (Fig. 4.3) and in many heating systems using so-called 'radiators'. Most of the heat from these radiators is in fact carried away by convection. It was also

Fig. 4.2 Sketch showing how fire may be spread in a building due to the conduction of heat along an unprotected steel girder.

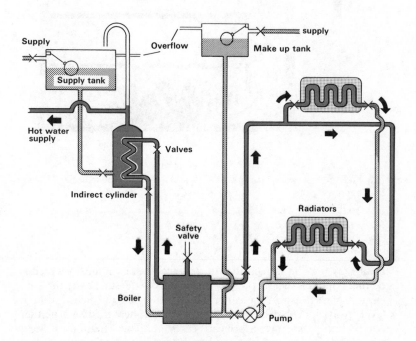

Fig. 4.3 Small bore heating and hot water system.

31

used in the 'thermo-syphon' system (now largely replaced by the pump-assisted system) of cooling motor engines. Convection also causes the up-draft in chimneys.

In a fire situation in a building, convection currents can convey hot gases produced by combustion upwards through stairwells (Fig. 4.4) and open lift shafts thereby spreading fire to the upper parts of buildings. In turn a current of cool air towards the fire replaces the hot gases rising from it, and helps to accelerate the burning.

Fig. 4.4 Sketch showing how fire on a lower floor can spread to upper floors by convection.

3 Radiation

Heat may also be transmitted in straight lines by a means which is neither conduction nor convection. Heat from the sun passes through empty space to warm the earth. Heat from a heater placed at high level in a room can be felt underneath the heater, where neither conduction nor convection can carry it. This method of heat transmission is named *radiation* and does not involve any contact between bodies and is independent of any material in the intervening space. It is one of the effects of electro-magnetic wave motions which include long wave length radio, with wave lengths of 1500 to 3000 metres, short wave radio (about 15 metres), radar (a few centimetres), light (8×10^{-5} to 4×10^{-5} cm) and X-rays or gamma rays (10^{-9} to 10^{-11} cm). All these, when they are absorbed by the body, produce a heating effect which depends on the amount of energy absorbed. The radiant energy which is transmitted from the sun is mainly in the band of wave lengths which we call 'light', because they can be detected by the retina of the eye. But bodies which do not emit light may radiate heat as infra-red waves. These are wave lengths longer than those of light lying between 10^{-2} and 10^{-4} centimetres.

All forms of radiant energy travel in straight lines at 3×10^8 metres per second (m/s); this is the speed of light. The intensity falls off inversely as the square of the distance from the source of radiation. This means that at twice the distance the intensity is one quarter; at three times the distance, the intensity is one-ninth, and so on. The inverse square law can be understood by looking at Fig. 4.5. The

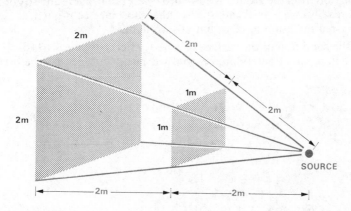

Fig. 4.5 Diagram showing the inverse square law as it applies to radiation.

square with 1 metre sides placed at, say, 2 metres from the source will throw a shadow with 2 metre sides on a second sheet placed 4 metres from the source. Thus the energy falling on 1 m² is the same as that which would have fallen on an area of $2\,m \times 2\,m = 4\,m^2$ at a distance of 4 metres. So the energy per square metre at 4 metres is one quarter that at 2 metres, i.e. one quarter at twice the distance. This is important when considering the effect of radiation from a heat source such as a fire.

When radiant energy (which, of course, includes infra-red radiation) falls on a body, there are three possibilities:

(a) Transmission

The energy passes through the body without warming it. The body is therefore 'transparent' to the energy.

33

b. Absorption

The energy is absorbed by the body, whose temperature is raised.

c. Reflection

The energy may be reflected back from the surface, e.g. reflection of light.

Some substances exhibit the phenomenon of 'selective absorption', that is, they allow some form of radiation to pass, but not others. Glass, for example, allows light to pass but absorbs infra-red radiation—hence glass may be used as a fire screen; the heat is stopped but the fire may be seen through it. (This is not intended to infer that glass is of much value as a fire barrier, as a number of other factors must be taken into account.) Carbon dioxide and water vapour also exhibit this property. Hence the sun's radiant energy (mainly in the form of light) falling on the earth passes through the atmosphere and warms the ground, while the resulting infra-red radiation from the ground is absorbed by the atmosphere and so does not readily escape back into space. Other substances, e.g. pitch, allow infra-red radiation to pass, but absorb light.

The condition of the surface of a body affects its ability to absorb or reflect radiation. White or polished metal surfaces are the best

Fig. 4.6 Clothing may be ignited by radiation when placed too close to a source of radiated heat.

reflectors, while matt black surfaces are bad reflectors. Good reflectors are bad absorbers and vice-versa. Hence the use in hot climates of white clothes, white-painted houses and cars and the like. Snow and ice, being white and good reflectors, are poor absorbers of heat and hence melt slowly in strong sunlight unless the surrounding temperature is raised sufficiently to cause heating by conduction or convection. Experiments have been carried out in which coal dust or other black powders have been spread on snow—the effect is to accelerate the melting because the sun's heat is more readily absorbed.

It is also found that a substance which is a good reflector of heat is a poor radiator of heat, and vice-versa. Thus a polished silver teapot retains its heat better than would a blackened teapot, in spite of silver being a good conductor. For the so-called radiators of a hot water system to radiate effectively they should be painted black, not a light colour as is usually the case.

Many fires have been caused by radiation—one of the most common is clothing being ignited by being placed too close to a source of radiation (Fig. 4.6), as sometimes happens when housewives are airing clothes on a clothes horse. Radiant heat from the sun passing through a glass window has sometimes been concentrated by an object inside the house which acts as a lens, a magnifying glass or a bottle, for instance, and this has been the cause of fire.

Part 2
The chemistry of combustion

Having dealt in Part 1 with the physical properties of matter and with heat, it is proposed in this Part to deal with the chemistry of combustion, but before passing to the subject in detail, it is necessary for the fireman to understand some of the basic concepts of chemistry. Chemistry is a complicated subject bristling with long and difficult names to pronounce, and with intricate formulae used by the chemist. There are, of course, many text books available to the student on chemistry, and in presenting this subject to the fireman as an opening to the study of fire-fighting techniques, it is difficult to decide exactly how much should be included. There have been numerous new processes and man-made materials introduced into industry and the home in the last decade or so, and so the fireman is faced with a great many new substances, particularly new building materials, when engaged in fire fighting, that he must of necessity have some idea how they will react when involved in fire. The particular hazards of many flammable materials and chemicals are dealt with separately in Parts 6B and 6C of the *Manual*, but in this Part it is proposed to deal with those aspects of chemistry as are applicable to his study of fire techniques, and to lead on to detail some of the more hazardous chemical substances from a purely chemical point of view.

Chapter 5
The basis of chemistry

Chemistry is the science of the composition of substances, their properties and reactions with each other. Substances may be solids, liquids or gases, in living or non-living systems, but all have one common factor—they consist of chemicals. The chemist recognises two distinct classes of substances; those which consist of a single chemical (elements and compounds) and those which are mixtures. A mixture may be separated into its constituents by some physical or mechanical means; for example, a mixture of salt and sand can be separated by dissolving the salt in water, leaving the sand behind. But to separate or change a single chemical substance, a chemical reaction is required.

1 Atoms and molecules

Whether the substance is single or a mixture, it is made up from many millions of very tiny particles which the chemist calls *molecules*. A mixture will contain more than one type of molecule, whereas a single chemical contains only one type of molecule. Molecules of the same substance are all exactly alike in their properties and behaviour.

A molecule may be defined as the smallest particle of a substance capable of existing independently.

The common substance chalk occurs in large quantities and in many different forms. For example, it is found in cliffs as lumps, or as a powder; it is, nevertheless, always recognisable as the same material, known chemically as *calcium carbonate*. This material is formed from innumerable calcium carbonate molecules. When the chemist investigates this molecule, he finds that it is composed of even smaller particles which he terms *atoms*. He also finds that every calcium carbonate molecule is exactly the same; each contains five atoms.

When we investigate other substances we find that their molecules also are formed from atoms. No matter how many substances we investigate, we will always find that the number of different atoms comprising their molecules is relatively small. The molecules of all substances comprise various combinations of atoms, from an overall range of approximately 100 different types of atom.

Atoms are the foundation of all substances. Unlike molecules, which can be broken down or changed during chemical reactions, atoms cannot be split *chemically* into anything smaller, although they can be split by nuclear bombardment, and this subject is dealt with in the *Manual, Part 6C: Section 11, 'Radioactive Materials'*. During chemical reactions the atoms rearrange to form different molecules, but the atoms themselves remain the same. They are the smallest particles to take part in chemical changes. Atoms are extremely small, their diameter being

between $\dfrac{1}{10\ 000\ 000}$ $\dfrac{4}{10\ 000\ 000}$ mm.

Substances formed entirely from one type of atom are called *elements*. There is an element corresponding to each different type of atom. Thus carbon, being formed entirely from carbon atoms, is an element. Similarly iron, containing only iron atoms, is another element. Elements may be composed of molecules made up from identical atoms joined together, or they may be composed of single atoms. The element oxygen consists of oxygen molecules, each molecule being two oxygen atoms joined together, whereas the element magnesium consists of single magnesium atoms.

When we again consider the molecule of calcium carbonate (chalk) we find that it is composed of one atom of the element calcium, one atom of the element carbon, and three atoms of the element oxygen, all chemically bound together. A list of the names of the elements is given in Table 3.

Table 3

List of the elements with atomic number,
atomic weight and valency

Name of element	Symbol	Atomic number*	Atomic weight*	Valency†
§Actinium	Ac	89	227	3
Aluminium	Al	13	27	3
Americium	Am	95	243	3, 4, 5, 6
Antimony (stibium)	Sb	51	122	3, 5
‡Argon	Ar	18	40	0
Arsenic	As	33	75	3, 5
Astatine	At	85	210	1, 3, 5, 7
Barium	Ba	56	137	2
Berkelium	Bk	97	249	3, 4
Beryllium	Be	4	9	2
Bismuth	Bi	83	209	3, 5
Boron	B	5	11	3
Bromine	Br	35	80	1, 3, 5, 7

Name of element	Symbol	Atomic number*	Atomic weight*	Valency†
Cadmium	Cd	48	112	2
Calcium	Ca	20	40	2
§Californium	Cf	98	251	
Carbon	C	6	12	2, 4
Cerium	Ce	58	140	3, 4
Caesium	Cs	55	133	1
Chlorine	Cl	17	35·5	1, 3, 5, 7
Chromium	Cr	24	52	2, 3, 6
Cobalt	Co	27	59	2, 3
Copper (cuprum)	Cu	29	63·5	1, 2
§Curium	Cm	96	247	3
Dysprosium	Dy	66	162·5	3
Einsteinium	Es	99	245	
Erbium	Er	68	167	3
Europium	Eu	63	152	2, 3
§Fermium	Fm	100	257	
Fluorine	F	9	19	1
Francium	Fr	87	223	1
Gadolinium	Gd	64	157	3
Gallium	Ga	31	70	2, 3
Germanium	Ge	32	73	4
Gold (aurum)	Au	79	197	1, 3
Hafnium	Hf	72	178·5	4
‡Helium	He	2	4	0
Holmium	Ho	67	165	3
Hydrogen	H	1	1	1
Indium	In	49	115	3
Iodine	I	53	127	1, 3, 5, 7
Iridium	Ir	77	192	3, 4
Iron (ferrum)	Fe	26	56	2, 3
‡Krypton	Kr	36	84	0
Lanthanum	La	57	139	3
Lawrencium	Lw	103	257	
Lead (plumbum)	Pb	82	207	2, 4
Lithium	Li	3	7	1
Lutecium	Lu	71	175	3
Magnesium	Mg	12	24	2
Manganese	Mn	25	55	2, 3, 4, 6, 7
§Mendelevium	Md	101	256	

Name of element	Symbol	Atomic number*	Atomic weight*	Valency†
Mercury (hydrargyrum)	Hg	80	201	1, 2
Molybdenum	Mo	42	96	3, 4, 6
Neodymium	Nd	60	144	3
§Neon	Ne	10	20	0
Neptunium	Np	93	237	4, 5, 6
Nickel	Ni	28	59	2, 3
Niobium	Nb	41	93	3, 5
Nitrogen	N	7	14	3, 5
§Nobelium	No	102	253	
Osmium	Os	76	190	2, 3, 4, 8
Oxygen	O	8	16	2
Palladium	Pd	46	106	2, 4, 6
Phosphorus	P	15	31	3, 5
Platinum	Pt	78	195	2, 4
Plutonium	Pu	94	242	3, 4, 5, 6
§Polonium	Po	84	210	2, 3, 4
Potassium (kalium)	K	19	39	1
Praseodymium	Pr	59	141	3
Promethium	Pm	61	145	3
§Protactinium	Pa	91	231	5
§Radium	Ra	88	226	2
‡Radon	Rn	86	222	0
Rhenium	Re	75	186	2, 3, 4, 6, 7
Rhodium	Rh	45	103	3
Rubidium	Rb	37	85·5	1
Ruthenium	Ru	44	101	3, 4, 6, 8
Samarium	Sm	62	150	2, 3
Scandium	Sc	21	45	3
Selenium	Se	34	79	2, 4, 6
Silicon	Si	14	28	4
Silver (argentum)	Ag	47	108	1
Sodium (natrium)	Na	11	23	1
Strontium	Sr	38	88	2
Sulphur	S	16	32	2, 4, 6
Tantalum	Ta	73	181	5
Technetium	Tc	43	99	6, 7
Tellurium	Te	52	128	2, 4, 6
Terbium	Tb	65	159	3
Thallium	Tl	81	204	1, 3

Name of element	Symbol	Atomic number$_5$	Atomic weight$_5$	Valency†
§Thorium	Th	90	232	4
Thulium	Tm	69	169	3
Tin (stannum)	Sn	50	119	2, 4
Titanium	Ti	22	48	3, 4
Tungsten (wolfram)	W	74	184	6
§Uranium	U	92	238	4, 6
Vanadium	V	23	51	3, 5
‡Xenon	Xe	54	131	0
Ytterbium	Yb	70	173	2, 3
Yttrium	Y	39	89	3
Zinc	Zn	30	65	2
Zirconium	Zr	40	91	4

* See section 4.   † See section 6.   ‡ Inert gases.

§ There is no unambiguous atomic weight for certain radioactive isotopes. Where there is a requirement to state the atomic weight, the mass number of the longest-lived isotope is often employed.

2 Compounds and mixtures

When two or more atoms of different elements are chemically bound together to form molecules, all exactly the same, the chemist says that a chemical *compound* has been formed. For example, each molecule of the compound calcium carbonate contains five atoms chemically bound together (one of calcium, one of carbon and three of oxygen).

The compound formed from identical molecules can only be broken down or changed by a rearrangement of the atoms, known as a *chemical reaction*. A mixture (formed from two or more different sorts of molecules) can be separated by physical or mechanical means into the substances which make up the mixture.

3 Symbols

Chemical symbols are used by chemists as a shorthand method of conveying information. The methods of using the symbols and of writing formulae are designed to give as much information as possible, whilst still being simple and quick to use.

43

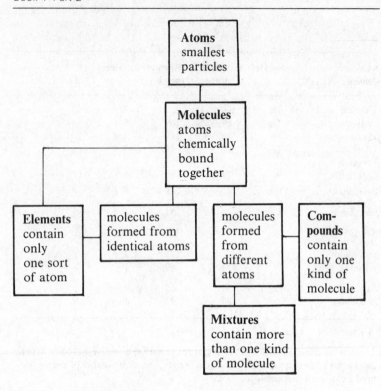

Every element is assigned a symbol (see Table 3), which is different from that of all the other elements. A symbol may be one letter or two; in the latter case the second letter is written as a small letter to avoid confusion. Thus the symbol for nickel is written Ni and not NI, as NI is not an element but represents nitrogen (N) and iodine (I). In many cases the symbols are the first letter of the name of the element, often followed by a second letter taken from that name. However, there are several common elements whose symbols bear no relationship to their modern names, since the symbols are based on the old Latin or Greek names. For example, the element sodium has the symbol Na which is derived from the Latin *natrium*, and silver has the symbol Ag, derived from *argentum*.

a. Use of symbols in writing formulae

When a symbol is written it represents one atom of the element. Thus:

    H   represents one atom of hydrogen;
    O   represents one atom of oxygen.

A group of symbols, called the formula, always represents one molecule of the substance and shows which atoms and how many of them are present in the molecule. Thus H_2O represents one molecule of water, containing two atoms of hydrogen and one atom of oxygen chemically bound together. Similarly CO_2 represents one molecule of carbon dioxide, containing one atom of carbon and two atoms of oxygen.

If a molecule contains more than one atom of the same type, the number of similar atoms is written at the bottom right of the appropriate symbol:

$CaCO_3$ — three atoms of oxygen

P_2O_5 — Two atoms of phosphorus

— five atoms of oxygen.

To represent more than one molecule we write a number in front of the formula as shown below

$3H_2O$ represents three molecules of water (and therefore a total of six hydrogen atoms and three oxygen atoms)

$3H_2O$

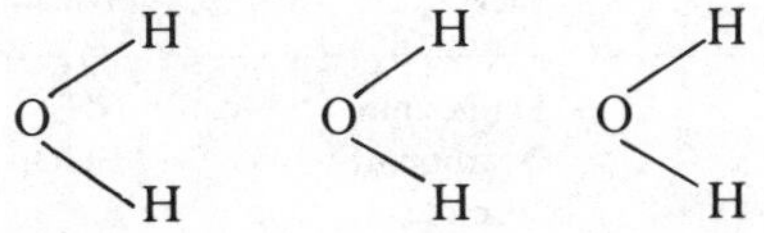

one water
molecule

$2MgO$ represents two molecules of magnesium oxide (and therefore a total of two magnesium atoms and two oxygen atoms)

$2MgO$ means   Mg — O   Mg — O

one magnesium
oxide molecule

b. Radicals

Certain groups of atoms, common to families of related compounds, are known as *radicals*. A radical may be defined as:

'A group of atoms present in a series of compounds which maintains its identity through chemical changes affecting the rest of the molecule.'

To show these radicals, formulae are often written with brackets enclosing the radical and with a number beyond the bracket to indicate how many times the radical appears in the formula. Radicals are not complete molecules and have no independent existence. For example, the formula of one molecule of calcium hydroxide (slaked lime) is $CA(OH)_2$. This shows the chemist the presence of the radical OH, whilst the number 2 indicates that this radical appears twice.

$$Ca(OH)_2 \text{ means } Ca \begin{matrix} \diagup OH \\ \diagdown OH \end{matrix}$$

i.e. there are two atoms of oxygen and two atoms of hydrogen in every calcium hydroxide molecule.

Similarly, the formula for aluminium nitrate is written $Al(NO_3)_3$

$$\text{meaning} \quad Al \begin{matrix} \diagup NO_3 \\ — NO_3 \\ \diagdown NO_3 \end{matrix}$$

A list of common radicals is given in Table 4.

Table 4

A list of common radicals

	Name	Symbol
Valency* 1	Ammonium	NH_4
	Bicarbonate	HCO_3
	Bromide	Br
	Chlorate	ClO_3
	Chloride	Cl
	Cyanide	CN
	Hydroxide	OH
	Iodine	I
	Nitrate	NO_3
	Nitrite	NO_2
	Perchlorate	ClO_4
Valency* 2	Carbonate	CO_3
	Sulphate	SO_4
	Sulphide	S
	Sulphite	SO_3
Valency* 3	Phosphate	PO_4

* See section 6

4 Atomic weight

To carry out chemical processes properly, the chemist must weigh the various substances. However, the weight of one atom or one molecule is extremely small—of the order of 10^{-22} grams, and so the actual weights of atoms are therefore of little practical use. It is more important to know how heavy one atom is in comparison with any other. The chemist therefore uses a relative atomic weight scale and not the actual weights of the atoms. Various scales have been proposed and, for technical reasons, the one most generally used is based on oxygen, which is given the atomic weight of 16·000. On this scale hydrogen has an atomic weight of 1·008. However, for normal purposes, the atomic weights can be rounded off, making hydrogen equal to 1 as shown in Table 1. We can then compare other atoms with hydrogen to see how many times heavier they are, so that we have the definition:

$$\text{Atom weight is } \frac{\text{the weight of one atom of the element}}{\text{the weight of one atom of hydrogen}}$$

For example, the atomic weight of sodium is 23 (written Na=23) and this signifies that one atom of sodium is 23 times as heavy as one atom of hydrogen.

5 Molecular weight

The same scale is used so that we compare the weight of one molecule with the weight of one atom of hydrogen.

$$\text{Molecular weight is } \frac{\text{the weight of one molecule of the substance}}{\text{the weight of one atom of hydrogen}}$$

For example, the molecular weight of water is 18 which means that one molecule of water is 18 times as heavy as one atom of hydrogen.

Since a molecule consists of atoms joined together, the weight of the molecule is that of its component atoms. Therefore, the molecular weight can be found by adding together the atomic weights of those atoms present, thus:

The molecular weight of sulphur dioxide (SO_2) is 64.

O(16)

S(32)

O(16)

Molecular Wt=atomic weight of sulphur +
2× atomic weight of oxygen
=32 + (2 × 16)
=64

Similarly: nitric acid HNO_3, molecular weight 63;

O(16)

H(1)——O(16)——(N(14)

O(16)

Molecular Wt=atomic weight of hydrogen +
atomic weight of nitrogen +
3× atomic weight of oxygen
=1 + 14 + (3 × 16)
=63

6 Valency

When atoms combine to form molecules they do so in definite fixed ratios. For example, one sodium (Na) atom always combines with one chlorine (Cl) atom to give NaCl (salt), but one magnesium (Mg) atom combines with two chlorine (Cl) atoms to give $MgCl_2$ (magnesium chloride). The 'combining power' of an atom depends on the arrangement and number of its electrons, but this will not be discussed here. The results of experiments which have determined the combining powers of atoms will be used and these powers will be quoted as numbers. These numbers are known as the *valency*, which tells us how many chemical bonds the particular atom, or group of atoms (radicals) will form. Valencies of all the elements are given in Table 3.

When molecules are formed, the atoms or radicals generally combine in ratios which balance out the valencies. This property enables us to work out the correct formulae of many chemical compounds. For example:

Magnesium oxide

Mg   valency 2

               giving

O   valency 2

To balance the valencies we need one Mg atom and one O atom; hence, magnesium oxide has the formula MgO.

Potassium carbonate

K   valency 1   K——

             giving CO_3

CO_3 valency 2   K——

Two K atoms are required to balance one CO_3 radical, and potassium carbonate therefore has the formula K_4CO_3.

Aluminium sulphate

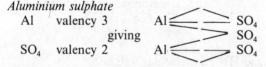

Al   valency 3

              giving

SO_4 valency 2

In this case two Al atoms are required to balance three SO_4 radicals (total bonds 6), and the formula of aluminium sulphate is therefore $Al_2(SO_4)_3$.

a. Multiple valency

Several elements, both metals and non-metals, show more than one valency. The valency used depends on the other elements with which the particular element is combined and on the conditions of the reaction in which the compound is formed; for example, heat, light, concentration. More detailed knowledge of the chemistry of the element is required to predict which valency will be used in any particular reaction. However, the names of the compounds formed are often adapted to help in deciding which valency is being used by the element in that particular compound, and hence to determine the correct formula.

b. Nomenclature

(1) –OUS and –IC

–OUS and –IC are used where an element shows two valencies. –OUS always indicates the lower valency and –IC the higher. For example:

Iron
Ferrous: valency 2,   e.g. $FeCl_2$ ferrous chloride
Ferric: valency 3,   e.g. $FeCl_3$ ferric chloride

Tin
Stannous: valency 2,   e.g. $SnBr_2$ stannous bromide
Stannic: valency 4,   e.g. $SnBr_4$ stannic bromide

(2) Use of Roman numerals

A modern approach to the problem of multiple valency is to indicate which valency is being used by inserting the appropriate Roman numeral after the name or symbol of the element concerned, e.g.

Iron (II)   chloride $Fe(II)Cl_2$
Iron (III) chloride $Fe(III)Cl_3$
Tin (II)   bromide $Sn(II)Br_2$
Tin (IV)   bromide $Sn(IV)Br_4$

(3) –IDE

–IDE is used to indicate that a compound is made up of two elements only. By convention, metals are written before non-metals in names and formulae, thus:

Magnesium oxide MgO
(Mg valency 2; O valency 2)
Potassium sulphide K_2S
(K valency 1; S valency 2)

–IDE is also used exceptionally for a few radicals, e.g. –OH hydroxide. Thus:

Calcium hydroxide $Ca(OH)_2$
(Ca valency 2; OH valency 1).

(4) –ITE and –ATE

–ITE and –ATE are used where a compound contains more than two elements, one of which is oxygen. For two related compounds, that named –ITE always possesses less oxygen than that named –ATE.

Sodium sulphite Na_2SO_3 (Na valency 1; SO_3 valency 2)
Sodium sulphate Na_2SO_4 (SO_4 valency 2)
Potassium nitrite KNO_2 (K valency 1; NO_2 valency 1)
Potassium nitrate KNO_3 (NO_3 valency 1)

The ending –ITE and –ATE are related to the ending –OUS and –IC where the latter are used in the names of acids. –OUS leads to –ITE and –IC to –ATE. For example:

Sulphurous acid H_2SO_3 gives sulphites — SO_3
Sulphuric acid H_2SO_4 gives sulphates — SO_4
Nitrous acid HNO_2 gives nitrites   — NO_2
Nitric acid HNO_3 gives nitrates   — NO_3

(5) Mono-, Di-, Tri-, Tetra-, Penta-

Mono-, di-, tri-, and penta- are used in names to tell how many of a particular atom or radical are present.

Mono-   =   1   e.g.   carbon monoxide CO
Di-   =   2   e.g.   carbon dioxide CO_2
Tri-   =   3   e.g.   sulphur trioxide SO_3
Tetra-   =   4   e.g.   carbon tetrachloride CCl_4
Penta-   =   5   e.g.   phosphorus pentachloride PCl_5

(6) Per-

Per- always denotes that there is more oxygen present in the compound than would normally be the case:

Hydrogen oxide (water) H_2O
Hydrogen peroxide H_2O_2
Sodium chlorate $NaClO_3$
Sodium perchlorate $NaClO_4$

7 Simple equations

Consider a simple chemical reaction. When sulphur (a yellow solid element) burns in air, it combines with oxygen from the air and a colourless gas with a pungent choking smell is formed. This gas is called sulphur dioxide (formula SO_2). These facts can be stated simply as:

Sulphur reacts with oxygen to form sulphur dioxide.

A further simplification can be made by replacing 'reacts with' by + and 'to form' by =. We then have

Sulphur   +   oxygen   =   sulphur dioxide
       (reacts with)   (to form)

This statement can be simplified even further by replacing the names of the chemicals by symbols and formulae. (The molecules of oxygen, like those of most common elements that are gases, contain two atoms, but sulphur, like other solid elements, is assumed to consist of single atoms.) This gives

$$S + O_2 = SO_2$$

This final statement represents the chemical equation for this reaction. It is a summary of the reaction, and tells us that every sulphur atom involved reacts with one oxygen molecule to form one sulphur dioxide molecule. It should be noticed that each side of the equation contains the same number of each type of atom present. This must always be the case since a chemical reaction involves a rearrangement of atoms and not their formation or disappearance.

Let us now take another example. Magnesium (a metal) burns in oxygen to form magnesium oxide (a white powder).

Magnesium reacts with oxygen to form magnesium oxide
Magnesium + oxygen = magnesium oxide
$Mg + O_2 = MgO$

In this case, although there is the same number of magnesium atoms on each side of the equation, this is not true in the case of the oxygen atoms, where there are two on the left-hand side and only one on the right-hand side. This implies that oxygen atoms disappear during the reaction. Chemical reactions never involve the creation or destruction of atoms, only their rearrangement. So in this case (and in many others) a procedure called balancing must be carried out before the equation is of any practical use. The equation above can be balanced in the following way:

Use two molecules of magnesium oxide instead of one:

$Mg + O_2 = 2MgO$

We now have equal numbers of oxygen atoms on each side of the equation, but the magnesium is 'out of balance'.

Use two atoms of magnesium on the left-hand side instead of one:

$2Mg + O_2 = 2MgO$

The equation is now correctly balanced, since each side contains equal numbers of each type of atom involved.

In balancing the equations, it is very important that the numbers of molecules used are altered, and not the formulae of the molecules themselves. For instance, it is quite wrong to go from $Mg + O_2 = MgO$ to $Mg + O_2 = MgO_2$ by altering the formula of magnesium oxide, which is known to be MgO. We can only get two atoms of oxygen on the right-hand side by using two molecules of MgO, as shown earlier.

8 Use of chemical equations

The balanced equation: $2Mg + O_2 = 2MgO$ tells us that two atoms of magnesium react with one molecule of oxygen to produce two molecules of magnesium oxide. These atoms and molecules have weights which are expressed in terms of their atomic and molecular weights (as described in section 3). The atomic weight of magnesium is 24, that of oxygen is 16, and if we use this information together with the equation, we obtain:

2 Mg	+	O_2	=	2MgO
2 × 24		2 × 16		2 (24 + 16)
48 units		32 units		80 units
(Two magnesium units)		(Two oxygen atoms)		(Two MgO molecules each containing 1 magnesium and 1 oxygen atom)

The 'units' are, of course, weight units, where one unit represents the weight of one hydrogen atom. Therefore, according to the equation, 48 units of magnesium will react with 32 units of oxygen to form 80 units of magnesium oxide. In other words the ratio:

$$\frac{\text{weight of magnesium}}{\text{weight of oxygen}} = \frac{48}{32}$$

Now an actual reaction between magnesium and oxygen will obviously involve millions of molecules of each substance. Suppose we 'scale up' this reaction until we have two million magnesium atoms instead of two. Then the magnesium atoms will react with one million oxygen atoms instead of just one.

Two atoms of magnesium weigh 48 units, therefore, two million atoms of magnesium weigh 48 × 1 000 000 units. Similarly, one molecule of oxygen weighs 32 units; therefore one million molecules of oxygen weigh 32 × 1 000 000 units, so that the ratio:

$\frac{\text{weight of magnesium}}{\text{weight of oxygen}}$ will again be $\frac{48}{32}$. No matter to what extent

the amounts of magnesium and oxygen are scaled up, the ratio

$\frac{\text{weight of magnesium}}{\text{weight of oxygen}}$ will always be $\frac{48}{32}$. Therefore:

If 48 grams of magnesium are used, 32 grams of oxygen are needed.

and 80 grams of magnesium oxide will be produced. For any other weight of magnesium, the weights of oxygen needed and magnesium oxide produced can be found by simple proportion.

9 Limitations of chemical equations

a. Reality

A chemical equation must be a summary of a known chemical reaction. For instance it is perfectly possible to write down the equation

$$\underset{\text{copper}}{Cu} + \underset{\text{nitric acid}}{2HNO_3} = \underset{\text{copper nitrate}}{Cu(NO_3)_2} + \underset{\text{hydrogen}}{H_2}$$

but such an equation is valueless because it is found that when nitric acid is added to copper, hydrogen is never produced. Therefore the equation is not 'telling the truth'.

b. Physical state

Equations say nothing about the physical state of the chemicals, whether they are solids, liquids or gases; whether they are pure substances or are dissolved in water or some other solvent; or whether the solutions are dilute or concentrated.

c. Reaction conditions

Equations say nothing about the reaction conditions; whether heat must be used or pressure applied.

d. Heat

Equations do not tell us whether heat is given out or absorbed during a chemical reaction.

e. Rate of reaction

Equations say nothing about the rate of the reaction; whether it is a slow reaction or a violent one; or whether or not a catalyst* must be used to speed up the reaction to a reasonable rate.

---

* A catalyst is a substance that alters the rate of a chemical reaction, but does not itself undergo a chemical change.

Chapter 6
Combustion

Combustion is a chemical reaction, or series of reactions, in which heat and light are evolved. When the rate of reaction is very slow only heat is evolved and a slow oxidation occurs, such as rusting. Combustion represents a rapid rate of reaction in which light is emitted as well as heat.

One way of discussing combustion is in terms of the triangle of combustion (Fig. 6.1). It is considered that for combustion to occur three factors are necessary: heat, oxygen and a combustible substance or fuel. Combustion will continue as long as these three factors are present. Removal of one of them leads to the collapse of the triangle, and combustion stops.

Fig. 6.1 The triangle of combustion.

Combustible substances exist as solids, liquids and gases. The burning of most materials produces a flame; this occurs when gases or vapours given off by a liquid or solid material are ignited. There are instances of solid state burning in which surface burning occurs with little or no visible liquid or vapour film. Indeed, for an explosive combustion, the greatest efficiency results from the conversion of the solid state to the gaseous state in the minimum amount of time.

1 Factors involved in combustion

An oxidation is said to be a reaction which involves combination with oxygen or other oxidising agents. The following reactions are typical examples of combustion:

(i) The oxygen may be supplied by the air.

$$C \quad + \quad O_2 = CO_2 \quad \text{carbon dioxide}$$
$$2CO + O_2 = 2CO_2$$
$$2H_2 + O_2 = 2H_2O$$

(ii) The combustion may take place using oxygen which is contained within the burning material, the combustible material and the supporter of combustion being together in the same compound.

$$4C_3H_5(NO_3)_3 = 12CO_2 + 10H_2O + 6N_2 + O_2$$
nitro glycerine

(iii) Oxygen may be provided by one of the materials in a mixture of compounds. The 'thermite reaction' illustrates this principle:

$$Fe_2O_3 + 2Al \longrightarrow Al_2O_3 + 2Fe + heat$$
thermite
mixture

(iv) Elements other than oxygen may be considered as oxidising agents; examples of this are chlorine and fluorine. Thus combustion may occur with these substances. Hydrogen will burn explosively with chlorine:

$$H_2 + Cl_2 \longrightarrow 2HCl$$

Many organic (i.e. materials based on the chemistry of carbon) materials will burn readily in halogen gases:

$$C_{10}H_{16} + 8Cl_2 \longrightarrow 16HCl + 10C$$
turpentine

Nitrogen is not usually thought of as an oxidising agent or even a reactive element, but some metals will burn vigorously in this gas. Magnesium, aluminium and their alloys form nitrides in combustion reactions:

$$3Mg + N_2 \longrightarrow Mg_3N_2$$
magnesium nitride

2 Heat of reaction and calorific value

All combustion reactions, such as those quoted above, involve giving out heat and are therefore called exothermic reactions. The quantity of heat produced per unit weight of fuel can be calculated, and is known as the *calorific value* of the fuel. For example, when 12 grams of carbon are burned to carbon dioxide 392 920 joules of heat are produced. Thus, the calorific value for carbon is $\dfrac{392\,920}{12} = 32\,813$ joules per gram (J/g).

Other factors must be considered in conjunction with the quantity of heat released in a chemical reaction. For example, the burning of magnesium produces less heat than the burning of carbon. When rates of reaction are considered, we find magnesium has a much higher rate of combustion than carbon so that the heat is released much more rapidly.

3 The nature of flame

As has been stated, the burning of most materials produces a flame. Flame may be defined as 'a reaction having the ability to propagate (or spread) through an atmosphere with the emission of heat and light'.

The exact nature of the propagation of flame is not fully understood, but the flame front may be thought of as a transition region separating burnt from unburnt gases. Light is usually given out from this region. A fuel-oxidant mixture which liberates enough energy on combustion to allow flame to spread through the unignited region of the mixture is called *flammable*.

A flame front stemming from a local ignition source is established in a flammable medium. A form of chemical reaction is set up in the layer of gas adjacent to this source with the result that heat and what are called *chain carriers* pass into the next layer of gas and continue the cycle of operations there, rather like runners in a relay race. Chain carriers are believed to be atoms or parts of molecules known as *free radicals* and these are extremely reactive. Combustion is a type of reaction known as *chain-reaction*.

Flames have varying structures, depending on the gas or vapour being burned. The differing zones in a flame are often characterised by the type of reaction going on in each zone. Very often flames are relatively starved of oxygen. The difficulty of supplying air or oxygen forces the volatile combustible matter to go far in search of air or oxygen and the result is a long flame. In the absence of oxygen within certain zones of the flame, the organic (carbon-containing) materials are decomposed by heat giving rise to tarry and sooty decomposition products. In other words, smoke is formed. In addition carbon monoxide is formed due to incomplete combustion.

It was stated earlier that most solids and liquids have to be heated above normal temperature before flammable vapours are emitted. In discussing combustion of such materials, several terms are used which are defined below.

4 Ignition temperature

a. Flash point

Flash point is the lowest temperature at which there is sufficient vaporisation of the substance to produce a vapour which will flash momentarily when a flame is applied. There are several types of apparatus for determining the flash point of a material (Abel, Pensky-Martin) and where necessary both the method and the type of apparatus is quoted (e.g. Abel, closed cup). It should be noted that this temperature will be affected by atmospheric pressure and that in some fire situations conditions might exist in which the pressure is under one atmosphere; this will result in a reduction in flash-point temperature.

b. Fire point

This may be defined as: 'the lowest temperature at which the heat from the combustion of a burning vapour is capable of producing sufficient vapour to enable combustion to continue'. It will be seen that the difference between flash point and fire point is that the flash point temperature is only required to produce vapour to enable a momentary flash to take place, whereas the fire point temperature has to be high enough to produce sufficient vapour to sustain the reaction, so that the substance continues to burn independently of the ignition source.

c. Spontaneous ignition temperature

This is the lowest temperature at which the substance will ignite spontaneously, that is the substance will burn without the introduction of a flame or other ignition source. This is sometimes referred to as the *ignition temperature*. This implies that under certain conditions some materials undergo spontaneous combustion.

d. Spontaneous combustion

Certain materials, especially organic materials based on carbon, may react with oxygen at room temperature. Compounds such as linseed oil which contain carbon-carbon double bands are very prone to this reaction. If the fuel is a good thermal insulator, the heat generated in such a reaction cannot get away, the temperature rises which increases the rate of reaction and the situation escalates. Eventually the ignition temperature is reached and true combustion commences.

Alternatively the action of bacteria on certain organic materials can cause a rise in temperature eventually leading to active combustion. A fine state of sub-division, as in powdered coal and some metals, could lead to spontaneous combustion. Many practical examples of the above phenomena have been recorded with drying oils, haystacks and coal stores. The thermal insulation factor is obviously of great importance in this type of combustion. Cross-linking of some plastics can lead to spontaneous combustion.

5 Limits of flammability

A flammable gas or vapour will only burn in air if the composition lies between certain limits. If too much, or too little, fuel is present burning will not take place; the mixture is said to be either too lean or too rich. These limits are referred to as the lower and upper limits of flammability. The lower limit is defined as the lowest concentration of fuel that will just support a self-propagating flame. The upper limit is defined as the highest concentration of fuel that will just support a self-propagating flame. Table 5 shows some typical limits of flammability; more will be found in the *Manual, Part 6C: Section 16.*

Table 5

Limits of flammability (percentage fuel/air by volume)

Gas	Lower limit	Upper limit
Hydrogen	4·1	74
Carbon monoxide	12·5	74·2
Methane	5	15
Butane	1·5	9
Ethylene	2·7	28·6
Acetylene	2·5	80

The figures quoted for limits of flammability often vary as there is a number of variable factors which may slightly alter the value. Pressure, temperature, dimensions of test apparatus, direction of flame propagation and moisture control of the mixture all have some effect.

6 Hazards of oxidising agents

Nearly all combustion reactions involve oxidation which in its most simple form is combination with oxygen, such as the combustion of carbon:

$$C + O_2 = CO_2$$

The oxygen in this case may be called an oxidising agent. The word oxidation also has a broader meaning where elements other than oxygen may be considered as oxidising agents. For example most metals will react with chlorine, or other halogens, and this is also a type of oxidation.

$$Mmg + Cl_2 = MgCl_2$$

Here chlorine is the oxidising agent.

There are certain compounds which do not necessarily burn themselves but, on decomposition, release oxygen which can greatly assist a combustion reaction. Some of these compounds may be relatively stable at room temperature but at elevated temperatures they could be extemely hazardous. Some of the more common oxidising agents are considered below.

a. Nitric acid and the inorganic nitrates

Concentrated nitric acid is a very powerful oxidising agent and reacts vigorously with many organic (carbon-based) compounds. Carbon itself reacts with the hot acid, thus:

$$C + 4HNO_3 = CO_2 + 4NO_2 + 2H_2O$$

Interaction of the concentrated acid with carbonaceous material involves a vigorous exothermic reaction with the evolution of nitrogen dioxide (nitrous fumes). Sawdust and wood chippings must not be used to soak up this acid. The nitrates (salts of nitric acid) are also good oxidising agents. They are used industrially and agriculturally and may be found in large quantities. An example is the use of molten nitrate salt baths for treating metals (see the *Manual, Part 6C: Section 7*), and the considerable use of certain nitrates as fertilisers (see *Part 6B: Chapter 1, 'Rural Fires'*).

On strong heating the nitrates of sodium and potassium give oxygen and the metal nitrite:

$$2KNO_3 = 2KNO_2 + O_2$$

Most other metal nitrates decompose to the metal oxide with evolution of nitrogen dioxide ('nitrous fumes') and oxygen. Ammonium nitrate is widely used as an agricultural fertiliser under various trade names. It is a white crystalline solid, very soluble in water (all nitrates are soluble in water). It does not burn but decomposes violently when heated giving nitrous oxide:

$$NH_4NO_3 = N_2O + 2H_2O$$

Under certain conditions explosions may occur. Brown nitrous fumes (NO_2) are also given off on heating; decomposition is complex. Because nitrous oxide will support combustion in a similar manner to oxygen, this decomposition produces conditioning for oxidation in a similar way as other nitrates.

b. Permanganates

The sodium ($NaMnO_4$) and potassium ($KMnO_4$) compounds are the most common. They are powerful oxidising agents and react with oxidisable organic materials, very often in a violent manner. This is seen in the reaction with glycerol (glycerine) where spontaneous ingition occurs. With concentrated hydrochloric acid, permanganates produce the highly toxic chlorine gas as a result of oxidation.

c. Chlorates

Chlorates are often used as their sodium or potassium compounds. On heating oxygen is evolved:

$$2KClO_3 \longrightarrow 2KCl + 3O_2$$

Very violent reactions occur on contact with oxidisable materials and may occur merely by friction. Potassium perchlorate ($KClO_4$) might appear to be a similar type of substance, but is, in fact, stable. Anhydrous perchloric acid ($HClO_4$) is a powerful oxidising agent and will explode on heating. Sodium chlorate is used as a weed killer. It has also been used in home-made explosives.

d. Chromates and dichromates

The most common compounds of this type are potassium chromate (K_2CrO_4) and potassium dichromate ($K_2Cr_2O_7$); these materials are yellow and orange respectively and are oxidising agents. They are soluble in water and will produce a highly combustible mixture with oxidisable substances.

e. Inorganic peroxides

Peroxides are a group of compounds which contain a higher proportion of oxygen than the 'normal' oxide. This extra oxygen is easily liberated, making these compounds good oxidising agents. Inorganic peroxides may be considered to derive from hydrogen peroxide (H_2O_2). Pure hydrogen peroxide is a clear viscous liquid with a specific gravity of 1·46 (at 0°C). It is soluble in water and is used at various concentrations. Above 70 per cent concentration in water it is a powerful oxidising agent and decomposes explosively:

$$2H_2O_2 \longrightarrow O_2 + 2H_2O$$

This decomposition may occur on heating, but may also be initiated by the presence of a catalyst. Small traces of metallic dust, charcoal or even strong light may be sufficient. Concentrated solutions of hydrogen peroxide are often known as 'high test peroxide' (HTP).

Common metal peroxides, derived from hydrogen peroxide, are those of sodium (Na_2O_2) and barium (BaO_2). Sodium peroxide is a pale yellow solid which reacts vigorously with water, releasing oxygen:

$$2Na_2O_2 + 2H_2O = O_2 + 4NaOH$$

A great deal of heat is liberated in this reaction and this could cause a fire in adjacent combustible material, and obviously the fire would be increased by the oxygen evolved.

Sodium peroxide can absorb carbon dioxide and release oxygen at the same time:

$$2Na_2O_2 + 2CO_2 \longrightarrow 2Na_2CO_3 + O_2$$

f. Organic oxidising agents

When nitric acid reacts with organic (carbon-based) compounds, two important types of substance are formed: organic nitrates ($-NO_3$) and nitro-compounds ($-NO_2$). These compounds are oxidising agents and furthermore they carry oxidisable carbon-containing material within their own molecules. Consequently, both the organic nitrates and the nitro-compounds are flammable. Some that contain several nitrate or nitro goups in the molecule are explosive, and typical examples are glyceryl trinitrate (used in dynamite) and trinitrotoluene (TNT)—an important military explosive.

Most organic nitrates and nitro-compounds are toxic and many of them, including glyceryl trinitrate, may be absorbed through the skin.

g. Organic peroxides and hydroperoxides

The structure of these compounds can be derived from that of hydrogen peroxide (H-O-O-H), by replacing both hydrogen atoms by organic groups, thus forming an organic peroxide. If only one hydrogen is replaced, a hydroperoxide is formed. As would be expected peroxides and hydroperoxides are powerful oxidising agents and because there is a carbon-containing part of the molecule which can be oxidised, they are highly flammable. Many of them are explosive and sensitive to heat and mechanical shock. Because of this they are often diluted or 'damped down' with either water or stable esters. Peroxides are extensively used as catalysts, especially in the plastics industry. Peroxides are toxic and are especially irritating to the skin, eyes and mucous membranes. Skin contact and breathing of vapours should be avoided. In all respects, organic peroxides and hydroperoxides should be treated with extreme caution.

Chapter 7
Combustible organic substances

Carbon forms a very large number of compounds, many of them with a small number of other elements such as hydrogen, oxygen, nitrogen and the halogens. It is convenient to divide chemistry into two branches, comprising organic chemistry which deals with the chemistry of the carbon compounds, and inorganic chemistry which deals with all the other elements. Carbon forms a much greater number of stable compounds with other elements than does any other element. There are believed to be over a million such compounds, which explains why a separate branch of chemistry is necessary to study them.

Carbon atoms differ from almost every other type of atom in that they are able to link up with other carbon atoms and form chains and rings. Most other atoms only join with others of the same kind in twos or threes. In all these organic compounds the valency of carbon is always four.

Organic chemicals are divided into two classes:

(i) aliphatic compounds, which contain chains of carbon atoms, and

(ii) aromatic compounds which contain a special kind of ring of six carbon atoms, known as a benzene ring.

Most organic chemicals are capable of burning. Indeed, many of our most important fuels, such as natural gas, petrol, paraffin and diesel oil are organic compounds.

1 Aliphatic compounds
(hydrocarbons: the paraffins)

The paraffin hydrocarbons are compounds containing carbon and hydrogen only. The simplest compound in the series is methane, the main constituent of natural gas. It has the formula CH_4 and the structure of the molecule represented as:

$$
\begin{array}{c}
\text{H} \\
| \\
\text{H} — \text{C} — \text{H} \\
| \\
\text{H}
\end{array}
$$

This representation denotes that the carbon atom uses each of its four valencies to join it to a hydrogen atom, which has a valency of one. The CH_4 molecule can also be regarded as a combination of the group:

$$
\begin{array}{c}
\text{H} \\
| \\
\text{H} \!-\!-\! \text{C} \!-\!-\!-\! \qquad \text{called a methyl group} \\
| \\
\text{H}
\end{array}
$$

with a hydrogen atom. Methane has well-defined chemical and physical properties and some of the latter are listed in Table. 6. Methane is a relatively unreactive gas, apart from its reaction with oxygen. It is flammable and forms explosive mixtures with air. The products of combustion, as with other hydrocarbons, are carbon dioxide and water:

$$CH_4 + 2O_2 = CO_2 + 2H_2O.$$

Larger molecules are built up by linking the carbon atoms together in chains, hydrogen atoms being attached to the carbon atoms in accordance with the valency rules. For example:

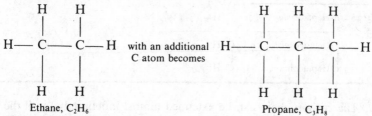

Methane, CH_4 with an additional C atom becomes   Ethane, C_2H_6

Ethane (C_2H_6) is another gas which is a constituent of natural gas. Because of the larger molecule, the physical properties differ from those of methane (see Table 5). The boiling point, melting point and vapour density of ethane are higher than those of methane, whereas the spontaneous ignition temperature of ethane is lower than that of methane.

A further increase in the chain-length of the molecule results in propane (C_3H_8), a constituent of liquefied petroleum gas:

Ethane, C_2H_6 with an additional C atom becomes   Propane, C_3H_8

Propane is chemically similar to ethane and methane, but once again, the physical properties differ (see Table 6).

Table 6 The paraffins

	Name	Formula	Structure
Gases	Methane	CH_4	$H-\underset{\underset{H}{\vert}}{\overset{\overset{H}{\vert}}{C}}-H$
	Ethane	C_2H_6	$H-\underset{\underset{H}{\vert}}{\overset{\overset{H}{\vert}}{C}}-\underset{\underset{H}{\vert}}{\overset{\overset{H}{\vert}}{C}}-H$
	Propane	C_3H_8	$H-\underset{\underset{H}{\vert}}{\overset{\overset{H}{\vert}}{C}}-\underset{\underset{H}{\vert}}{\overset{\overset{H}{\vert}}{C}}-\underset{\underset{H}{\vert}}{\overset{\overset{H}{\vert}}{C}}-H$
	Isomers:		
	n-Butane	C_4H_{10}	$H-\underset{\underset{H}{\vert}}{\overset{\overset{H}{\vert}}{C}}-\underset{\underset{H}{\vert}}{\overset{\overset{H}{\vert}}{C}}-\underset{\underset{H}{\vert}}{\overset{\overset{H}{\vert}}{C}}-\underset{\underset{H}{\vert}}{\overset{\overset{H}{\vert}}{C}}-H$
	iso-Butane	C_4H_{10}	(branched structure)
Liquids	n-Pentane	C_5H_{12}	$H-\underset{\underset{H}{\vert}}{\overset{\overset{H}{\vert}}{C}}-\underset{\underset{H}{\vert}}{\overset{\overset{H}{\vert}}{C}}-\underset{\underset{H}{\vert}}{\overset{\overset{H}{\vert}}{C}}-\underset{\underset{H}{\vert}}{\overset{\overset{H}{\vert}}{C}}-\underset{\underset{H}{\vert}}{\overset{\overset{H}{\vert}}{C}}-H$
	n-Hexane	C_6H_{14}	$H-\underset{\underset{H}{\vert}}{\overset{\overset{H}{\vert}}{C}}-\underset{\underset{H}{\vert}}{\overset{\overset{H}{\vert}}{C}}-\underset{\underset{H}{\vert}}{\overset{\overset{H}{\vert}}{C}}-\underset{\underset{H}{\vert}}{\overset{\overset{H}{\vert}}{C}}-\underset{\underset{H}{\vert}}{\overset{\overset{H}{\vert}}{C}}-\underset{\underset{H}{\vert}}{\overset{\overset{H}{\vert}}{C}}-H$
	↓ n-Hexadecane	↓ $C_{16}H_{34}$	
Solids	n-Heptadecane	$C_{17}H_{36}$	
	n-Octadecane	$C_{18}H_{38}$	
	↓ n-Heptacontane	↓ $C_{70}H_{142}$	

The carbon chain can be extended almost indefinitely, until the carbon atoms in the molecule number many thousands, as in polyethylene. With each increase in the length of the carbon chain, and hence in the size of the molecule, there are corresponding

64

Melting point (°C)	Boiling point (°C)	Flash point (°C)	Flammable limits (% in air)	Self-ignition temperature (°C)
−183	−161	Gas	5 to 15	538
−172	−89	Gas	3·3 to 12·5	510
−187	−42	−104	2·4 to 9·5	466
−138·6	−0·6	−60	1·5 to 9·0	430
−160	−12	Gas	1·8 to 8·4	545
−130	36	<−40	1·4 to 7·8	309
−95·6 ↓ 18	69 ↓ 287	−7 ↓ >100	1·2 to 7·4 —	260 ↓ 205
22	303	—	—	200
28 ↓ 105	308 —	—	—	200 —

increases in the boiling and melting points. Consequently, we eventually arrive at compounds which are liquids at room temperature (e.g. pentane C_5H_{12}) and finally solids (e.g. hexadecane $C_{16}H_{34}$). Representative members of the series are listed in Table 5.

Compounds near C_8H_{18} are found in petrol, those near $C_{10}H_{22}$ in paraffin, those near $C_{14}H_{30}$ in diesel oil, those near $C_{18}H_{38}$ in petroleum jelly and those near $C_{25}H_{52}$ in paraffin wax.

The following points may be noted concerning these compounds:

(i) They form a series in which each differs from the next by one —CH_2 unit.

(ii) All members of the series have similar chemical properties.

(iii) The physical properties of all members of the series vary in a regular way throughout the series. As a number of carbon atoms increases, so the following also increase:

    melting point   vapour density
    boiling point   flash point

but solubility in water and spontaneous ignition temperature both decrease.

2 Unsaturated hydrocarbons

a. Olefines

There is another series of compounds known as *olefines*. The first member of the series is ethylene (C_2H_4), the formula for which is represented as:

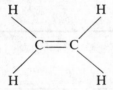

where there is a double bond between the two carbon atoms. The carbon still has its valency of 4 and hydrogen that of 1, but each carbon atom uses two of its valency bonds to link to the other carbon atom. Compounds containing double or triple bonds are termed *'unsaturated'*.

Unsaturated compounds are considerably more reactive than paraffins. They not only burn, but react readily with chlorine, hydrogen chloride, bromine, etc. For example:

$$\underset{\text{(Ethylene)}}{\overset{\displaystyle H \qquad H}{\underset{\displaystyle H \qquad H}{C = C}}} + Cl_2 \longrightarrow \underset{\text{(Ethylene dichloride or dichloroethane)}}{H - \overset{\displaystyle H}{\underset{\displaystyle Cl}{C}} - \overset{\displaystyle H}{\underset{\displaystyle Cl}{C}} - H}$$

The reactivity of ethylene makes it an important starting point in the production of plastics and other materials.

Other olefines can be obtained by progressively increasing the length of the carbon chain. As with the paraffins, the physical properties alter in a regular way as the size of the molecule increases (see Table 7).

b. Acetylenes

There are also substances known as acetylenes, in which a carbon-carbon triple bond is found. The only important member is the gas acetylene (C_2H_2). It is unsaturated compound and the only way of arranging the normal valency bonds of the carbon and hydrogen is

$$H—C \equiv C—H$$
Acetylene

Here, each carbon atom uses three valencies to join it to the other. This unsaturation is reflected in the great reactivity of acetylene, which is liable to explode on exposure to heat or mechanical shock, even when air or oxygen are absent. Acetylene is flammable and forms mixtures in air with a wide explosive range (2·5–80 per cent). Some of its physical properties are given in Table 8. Acetylene is used in the manufacture of plastics (e.g. pvc), other chemicals and in oxyacetylene welding. It is stored by dissolving it in acetone, which is absorbed in an inert porous material contained in cylinders.

3 Aromatic hydrocarbons

Another series of hydrocarbons are known as *aromatics*. These compounds are based on a ring structure of which the benzene ring is typical. The structure consists of six carbon atoms arranged in a ring, with alternating single and double bonds:

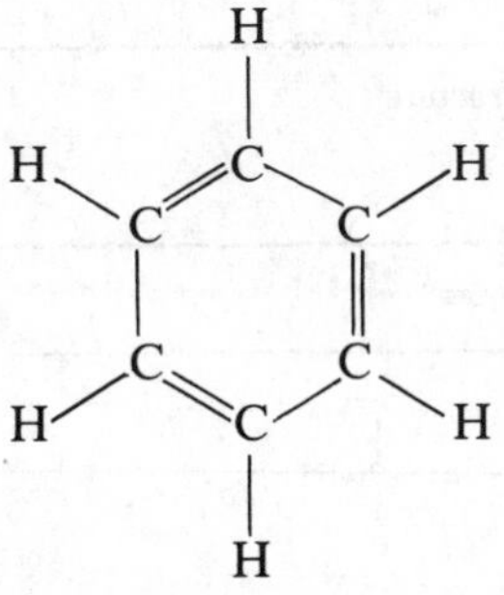

usually represented as

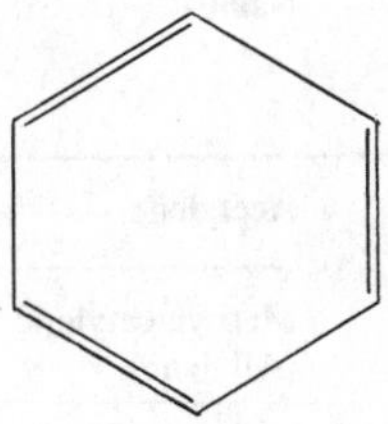

Benzene

Table 7 The olefines

Name	Formula	Structure
Ethylene	C_2H_4	
Propylene	C_3H_6	
The Butylenes	C_4H_8	
Gases		

*The olefines are liquids from C_5H_{10} to $C_{16}H_{32}$, and then solids.

Table 8 The acetylenes

Name	Formula	Structure
Acetylene	C_2H_2	H—C≡C—H
Methylacetylene (Allylene)	C_3H_4	
*Gases		

*The acetylenes are liquids from C_4H_6 to $C_{17}H_{32}$, and then solids.
†Sublimes.

Melting point (°C)	Boiling point (°C)	Flash point (°C)	Flammable limits (% in air)	Self-ignition temperature (°C)
−169	−103·9	Gas	2·7 to 28·6	450
−185	−48	Gas	2 to 11	495
About −185	About −6·3	<−80	1·7 to 10·0	384

Melting point (°C)	Boiling point (°C)	Flash point (°C)	Flammable limits (% in air)	Self-ignition temperature (°C)
−81	−84†	−17·7	2·5 to 80	335
−102·7	−23	Gas	1·7 to —	—

The double bonds are linked in a special way and benzene does not behave like an olefine. In fact, the benzene ring is quite stable, so that aromatic compounds, although more reactive than paraffins, are less reactive than olefines.

Benzene is a flammable compound, but because there is a high proportion of carbon in the molecule, there is usually not enough oxygen to oxidise all the carbon to carbon monoxide and carbon dioxide. Consequently, a good deal of carbon is released as thick black smoke. Aromatic compounds usually burn with a very smoky flame.

Other aromatic compounds are formed by replacing the hydrogen atoms by other atoms or groups of atoms, such as methyl radicals. For example:

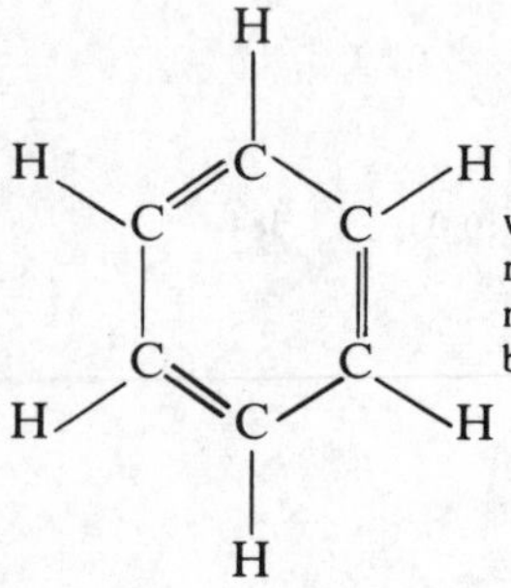

with one H atom replaced by a methyl radical, becomes

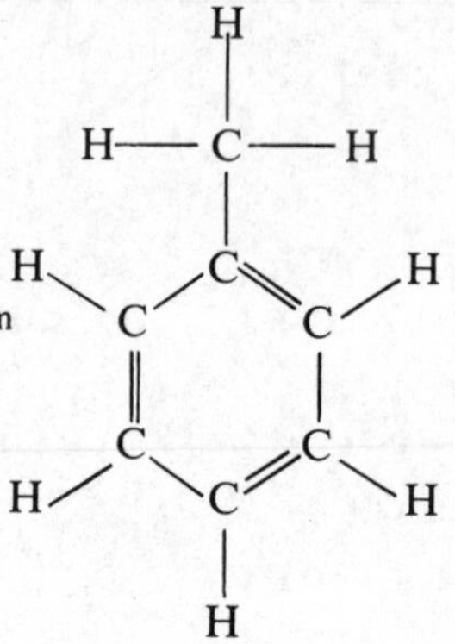

(Benzene, C_6H_6)

(Toluene, C_7H_8)

or

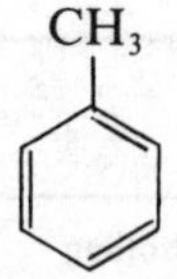

CH_3

Similarly:

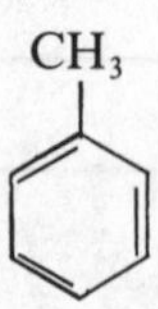

CH_3

with a further H atom replaced by a methyl radical, becomes

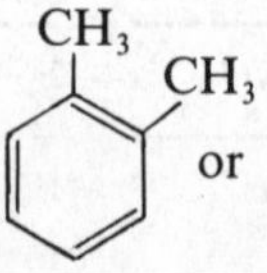

or

or

(Toluene, C_7H_8)

ortho-xylene (o-xylene)

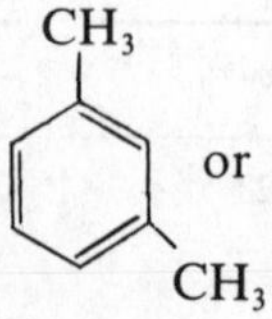

meta-xylene (m-xylene)

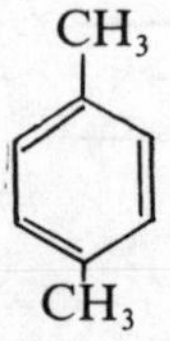

para-xylene (p-xylene)

The physical properties of the members of this series vary in a regular way as the molecular weight increases, but the chemical properties remain similar. Some aromatic compounds, especially toluene and the xylenes, are important solvents.

It is worth noting that hydrocarbons do not dissolve to any extent in water, and they usually float on water. Some aromatic compounds are toxic; benzene for example is highly toxic, both as a vapour and by skin absorption.

4 Liquefied petroleum gases

Propane (C_3H_8) and butane (C_4H_{10}) are gases at room temperature and pressure, but by the application of pressure may be liquefied. This is because the critical temperatures of these gases are well above room temperature and so they may be liquefied by pressure alone. A very small amount of liquid will produce a great volume of gas and so by liquefying the gas a great deal of it can be stored in a small volume. As both gases are highly flammable and are widely used as fuel gases, the installations containing the liquid gases are very widespread and may be expected to increase.

A most important property of LPG is the critical temperature—the temperature above which it is impossible to liquefy a gas by pressure alone. For propane, the critical temperature is 96·7°C and for butane, 152°C. When these liquefied gases are put in the right kind of container, they are self-sustaining. They will boil and produce vapour until the pressure rises enough in the container to prevent further production of gas for as the pressure on a liquid increases so does its boiling point. So inside each liquid gas container there is a liquid with pressurised gas above it. As the gas is withdrawn, the gas pressure would fall, but more liquid will evaporate to restore the pressure to its original value.

Table 6 shows some of the more important properties of propane and butane.

As has been stated both propane and butane are highly flammable. The amount of flammable vapour produced by an escape of propane may be considered when it is known that the ratio of liquid to gas for propane is 1 to 270. Both gases formed are heavier than air and will seek lower ground; they are odourless and colourless, and very frequently a stenching agent known as mercaptan is added. When propane and butane evaporate they require heat from their surroundings and in the case of propane this is easily supplied naturally, but in the case of butane this may not always be so in cold conditions as its boiling point is about the same as the surrounding air (ambient temperature) and it will fail to boil off to any degree. For this reason, mixtures of propane and butane are frequently used.

In dealing with LPG it is vital to realise that under no circumstances should the temperature rise above the critical temperature, as above this temperature the substances can only exist as gases. Cylinders heated above the critical temperature are therefore likely to explode.

Full details of the storage and fire-fighting techniques associated with liquefied petroleum gases will be found in the *Manual, Part 6C: Section 5, 'Fires in Fuels'*.

Chapter 8
Solvents

1 Alcohols

The structure of the alcohols is derived from the paraffin hydrocarbons, in which one of the hydrogen atoms is replaced by a hydroxyl group O—H;

<pre>
        H   H
        | |
H——— C———H   with one H atom replaced   H— C———O———H
        | by an O—H group becomes |
        H   H
    Methane,   Methyl alcohol
     CH₄   CH₃ OH (Methanol)
</pre>

Typical higher alcohols are ethyl alcohol or ethanol (C_2H_5OH), propyl alcohol or propanol (C_3H_7OH) and butyl alcohol or butanol (C_4H_9OH). As the molecular weight increases, there is a general increase in melting point, boiling point and flash point, accompanied by a decrease in solubility in water and in spontaneous ignition temperature. The first few members of the series dissolve completely in water but members higher than butyl alcohol are only slightly soluble. All alcohols are less dense than water and therefore the insoluble ones float on the top of it.

Chemically the alcohols resemble each other. The first members of the series are flammable liquids. Ethyl alcohol is sometimes used as a fuel and is also used in rocket propulsion systems. Alcohols are also used as intermediaries in various chemical processes. Methyl and ethyl alcohols are widely used as solvents in industry and ethyl alcohol is the most important ingredient of beer, wines and spirits. Propyl and butyl alcohols are also used as solvents and some of the higher alcohols are used to make detergents. Nearly all alcohols are to a greater or lesser extent toxic according to type.

2 Aldehydes

These compounds all contain the group

attached to such organic groups as methyl (CH_3—), ethyl (C_2H_5—) and so on. The simplest member of the group is formaldehyde

with the formula CH_2O. Formaldehyde is a colourless, flammable gas with a pungent suffocating smell. It is not often encountered as a gas and it is more usual to find it as a 4 per cent solution in water, which also contains a little methyl alcohol. This solution is often called formalin. The solution gives off flammable vapour if it is heated above its flash point, which varies according to the formaldehyde and methyl alcohol concentration. This vapour is toxic. Formaldehyde is used in the manufacture of several plastics, as an antiseptic and as a preservative of anatomical specimens.

The next member of the series, acetaldehyde (CH_3CHO) has the structure

$$H-\underset{\underset{H}{|}}{\overset{\overset{H}{|}}{C}}-\underset{H}{\overset{H}{C}}=O$$

It is a colourless liquid with a strong fruity smell. The compound dissolves readily in water, is flammable and toxic and the vapour forms explosive mixtures with air. It is used as an intermediate in the manufacture of other chemicals and plastics.

The other aldehydes are rather less important. The physical properties of these materials vary in the usual way as the molecular weight increases.

3 Ketones

The simplest ketone is acetone (C_2H_6CO) with the structure

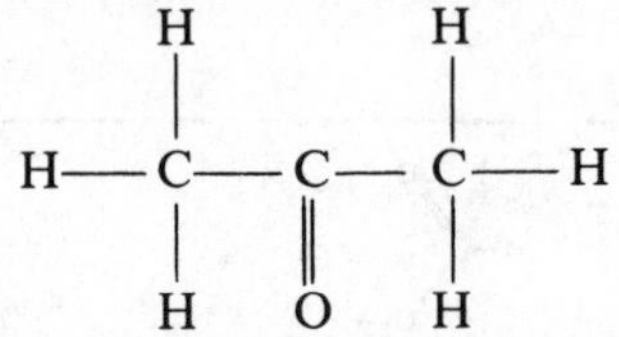

$$
\begin{array}{ccccc}
 & H & & & H \\
 & | & & & | \\
H- & C & -C- & C & -H \\
 & | & \| & & | \\
 & H & O & & H
\end{array}
$$

The formulae of the other members of the series can be obtained by lengthening the carbon chains in the usual way. Acetone is by far the most commercially important member of the series. It is a colourless, highly flammable liquid with a mint-like smell and dissolves readily in water. It is toxic to the extent that high concentrations have an anaesthetic effect and the liquid dissolves the fats out of the skin, and so can give rise to dermatitis and skin irritations. Acetone is a very important industrial solvent for materials such as paint removers, cellulose acetate, fats, waxes and acetylene.

The next member of the series is methyl ethyl ketone (MEK)

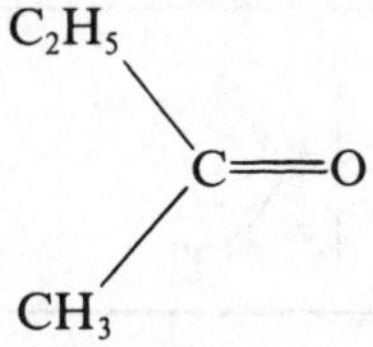

$$
\begin{array}{c}
C_2H_5 \\
\diagdown \\
\quad C=O \\
\diagup \\
CH_3
\end{array}
$$

It is another important industrial solvent and chemically resembles acetone in most respects. Ketones are fairly resistant to attack by oxidising agents but are nevertheless flammable.

4 Carboxylic acids

The carboxylic acids are known alternatively as the 'fatty acids' because they are related to the aliphatic hydrocarbons and have a similar chain structure. They all contain the group

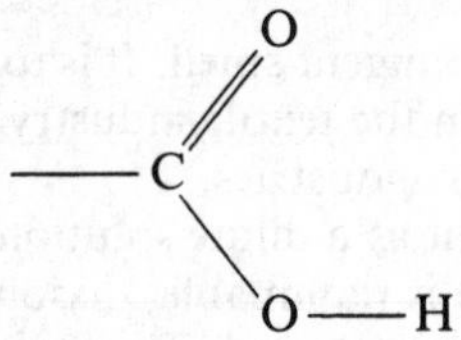

$$
\begin{array}{c}
\quad\quad O \\
\quad\quad \| \\
-C \\
\quad \diagdown \\
\quad\quad O-H
\end{array}
$$

which is attached to various organic groups such as methyl ($-CH_3$) and ethyl ($-C_2H_5$). The first member of the carboxylic acid series is formic acid

Table 9 Carboxylic acids

Name	Formula	Structure
Formic acid	HCOOH	$H-C\begin{smallmatrix}O\\\\O-H\end{smallmatrix}$
Acetic acid	CH₃COOH	structure
Propionic acid	C₂H₅COOH	structure
Butyric acid	C₃H₇COOH	structure

This is more frequently written HCOOH.

Formic acid is a colourless liquid with a pungent smell. It is toxic and can cause burns on the skin. It is used in the textile industry, in electroplating and in the leather and rubber industries.

Acetic acid (CH₃COOH), which is present as a dilute solution in vinegar, is the next member of the series. It is flammable, dissolves readily in water and can burn the skin if concentrated. The vapour and the concentrated acid is toxic. It is used as a solvent in chemical manufacture.

The properties of some of these acids are given in Table 9. They are all more or less weak acids.

76

Melting point (°C)	Boiling point (°C)	Flash point (°C)	Flammable limits (% in air)	Self-ignition temperature (°C)
8	101	69	—	600
16·6	118	45	4 (lower)	566
−22	141	54	—	—
−7·9	163·5	72	2 to 10	452

5 Esters

The ester series can be thought of as being derived from the carboxylic acids by the replacement of they hydrogen atom in the

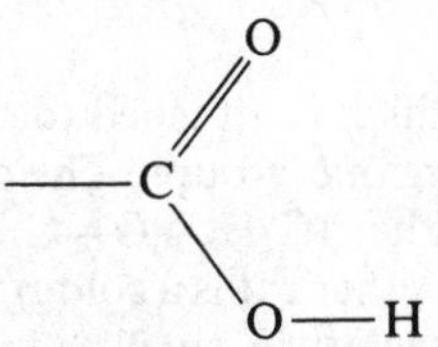

(COOH)

group by a methyl or other radical. For example:

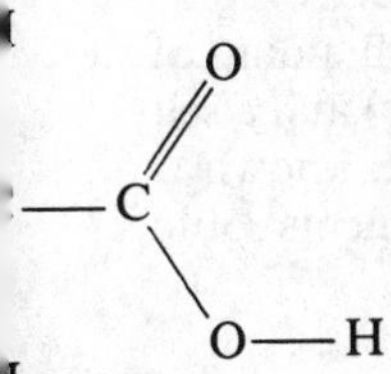

with the *H replaced by the ethyl radical C_2H_5, becomes

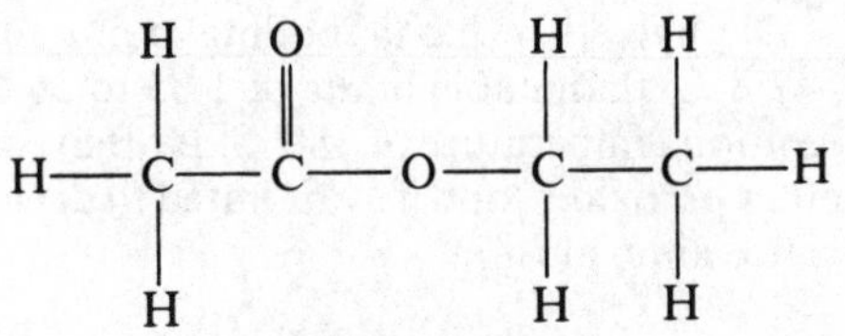

Ethyl acetate, $CH_3COOC_2H_5$

cetic acid, H_3COOH

77

Table 10 Esters

Name	Formula	Structure
Ethyl formate	$HCOOC_2H_5$	
Ethyl acetate	$CH_3COOC_2H_5$	
Ethyl butyrat	$C_3H_7COOC_2H_5$	
Amyl acetate	$CH_3COOC_5H_{11}$	

Esters are flammable, colourless liquids or solids and are usually only slightly soluble in water, on which they float. They have fruity smells and are often found in fruit and in scents. The higher solid member of the series are found in beeswax and spermaceti. The esters are used as solvents, and in pharmaceuticals, perfumery and foodstuffs. Some properties of a few esters are given in Table 10.

6 Ethers

These all contain the oxygen atom —O— which is attached to such groups as methyl, ethyl and vrious other organic groups. The only one of commercial significance is diethyl ether (C_2H_5—O—C_2H_5). This substance is often referred to merely as 'ether'. It is a colourless, highly flammable, volatile liquid with a characteristic smell. It is less dense than water and immiscible in it. It is toxic in high concentrations and at lower ones has an anaesthetic effect.

Diethyl ether has a boiling point of 34·5°C, a flash point of −42·8°C, flammable limits of 1·85 to 36·5 per cent (in air) and a self ignition temperature of 180°C. It often contains substances known as ether peroxides, and if evaporated to dryness these components could cause an explosion.

Melting point (°C)	Boiling point (°C)	Flash point (°C)	Flammable limits (% in air)	Self-ignition temperature (°C)
–79	–54	–20	2·8 to 16·5	455
–84	77	–4	2 to 11·5	<427
–93	121	25	—	463
–78·5	148	25	1·1 to —	399

Chapter 9
Plastics

1 The nature of organic solids polymers

Many organic solids, including wood, plastics and rubbers, are polymers. This means that the molecules of which they are composed consist of very long chains; these may contain many thousands of carbon atoms. Living things, such as trees, are able to create such molecules, as in the case of wood, but in the last seventy years chemists have been able to create or synthesise polymer molecules in the laboratory. Many of these have passed into commercial use as plastics and synthetic rubbers. The chemists have achieved this by taking small molecules with two or more reactive groups and arranging for these to link up end to end and form long chains. For example in ethylene $H_2C=CH_2$, the double band may break to give

$$\overset{\diagdown}{H_2C}-\!\!-\!\!\overset{\diagup}{CH_2}$$

which will very rapidly combine with other molecules of the same type to produce polyethylene

$$-CH_2-CH_2-CH_2-CH_2-CH_2-CH_2-$$

which consists of a long chain of $-CH_2-$ groups joined to each other. In a case such as this we call ethylene the *monomer* and polyethylene is the resultant *polymer*.

Simple straight-chain polymers of this type are well known; many of them have small-sided groups attached to the chain, as in polypropylene

$$\underset{\displaystyle CH_2-\!\!-\!\!CH}{\overset{\displaystyle CH_3}{\;\;\;\;\;\;\;\;\;\;|}}\underset{\displaystyle -\!\!-CH_2-\!\!-\!\!CH}{\overset{\displaystyle CH_3}{\;\;\;\;\;\;\;\;\;\;|}}\underset{\displaystyle -\!\!-CH_2-\!\!-\!\!CH}{\overset{\displaystyle CH_3}{\;\;\;\;\;\;\;\;\;\;|}}$$

or polystyrene

$$CH_2{-}CH{-}CH_2{-}CH{-}CH_2{-}CH$$

Here the symbol ⬡ stands for the benzene ring (see page 67).

Benzene rings are frequently referred to as aromatic structures. These straight-chain materials can be melted by heating to quite low temperatures of 100°C or so in many cases. Such materials are called *thermoplastics* and the process technology depends upon the fact that they soften or melt upon heating.

There is another class of plastics where heating will not melt the material, but will cause it to char and eventually to decompose. Such materials are referred to as *thermosetting* plastics. They have this property because the molecule is like an enormous three-dimensional network, or in other words, the long chains are also linked together sideways by carbon-carbon bands and the material is said to be cross-linked. Fig. 9.1 illustrates this point, the lines representing polymer molecules and their cross-links.

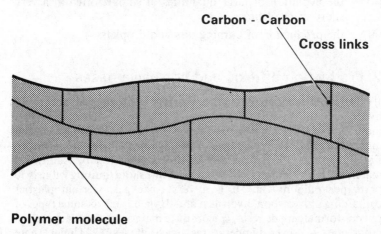

Fig. 9.1 The cross-links of polymer molecules of thermo-setting plastics.

Clearly the process technology of such materials cannot depend merely upon melting them to form a liquid, which is then processed. In fact a shorter chain polymer is produced, which may be moulded or cast by some means, and the molecules of this polymer have reactive chemical groups upon them. Under the influence of heat or catalysts, or indeed both of these, the active groups react together and cross-links are formed. Thus the finished thermosetting plastics is produced.

Plastics and rubbers are not always encountered in their pure state as they often have other materials mixed into them to improve their properties or to make them cheaper. Such materials are:

(1) Fillers
These are inert materials such as china clay, wood flour or perhaps carbon black. In laminated plastics the fillers may be sheets of paper of glass-cloth.

(2) Plasticisers
These are chemicals that can be mixed with some thermoplastics (notably pvc) to make them softer and possibly easier to process.

(3) Stabilisers
As the name suggests, these are added to prevent the polymer from being oxidised, attacked by sunlight or decomposed by mild heating.

(4) Colouring materials
These could be organic or inorganic.

When plastics and rubbers are overheated or in a fire situation, the following problems are of special interest to the fire fighter:

(i) the evolution of toxic and corrosive gases;

(ii) the evolution of large quantities of smoke, often in a very short space of time;

(iii) the production of burning tars and droplets.

2 Production of toxic and corrosive gases

If plastics only contain the elements carbon and hydrogen, or carbon, hydrogen and oxygen, the main gas to be expected is carbon monoxide (CO) which is formed when organic materials are burned in a relative shortage of oxygen. This gas is a well-known hazard to fire fighters as it is produced in the combustion of traditional materials. It is odourless, colourless, the threshold limiting value is 50 parts per million—thus it is a very toxic gas. Certain plastics containing only carbon, hydrogen and oxygen, such as some types of phenol-formaldehyde resin, can produce materials other than carbon monoxide at lower temperatures, such as 470°C. Under these conditions phenol is produced, which would present a toxic hazard.

82

If plastics contain nitrogen in addition to carbon, hydrogen or oxygen, we may expect nitrogen compounds in the fire gases; these are very probably toxic. Such nitrogen-containing materials are cellulose nitrate, nylon, polyurethane foams, melamine-formaldehyde plastics, urea-formaldehyde plastics, ABS (acrylonitrile-butadiene-styrene), some epoxy resins and nitrile rubbers. In the gases given off as a result of fire, the nitrogen of these materials may well appear as nitrogen dioxide, hydrogen cyanide and various organic nitriles (cyanides), all of which are toxic, especially so in the case of cyanides and nitriles.

Polyurethane foams have been extensively investigated and hydrogen cyanide and carbon monoxide are present in appreciable amounts in the fire gases. Less is known concerning the other materials, but there is a strong possibility that toxic nitrogenous compounds are present in the fire gases. In the case of cellulose nitrate, hyrogen cyanide, nitrogen oxide and carbon monoxide are known to be present.

Chlorine is an element present in polyvinyl chloride (pvc) and certain related co-polymers, in neoprene and in certain types of self-extinguishing fibre-glass polyester resin. In the case of pvc almost all the chlorine of the molecule appears as hydrogen chloride gas in the fire gases. This is both toxic and corrosive; it has a very sharp penetrating odour and with water it will form solutions of hydrochloric acid, which is also corrosive. Apart from corroding many metals, the acid may cause long term changes in alkaline mortar. Ferroconcrete may be much less affected; nevertheless, copious washing after incidents involving pvc is very desirable. Other chlorine-containing polymers may also give hydrochloric acid gas and possibly other chlorine-containing toxic compounds as well.

Fluorine-containing polymers are p.t.f.e. (polytetrafluoro-ethylene), certain related materials, such as 'Kel-F' and a series of synthetic rubbers, sometimes known as 'vitons'. If these materials are overheated, toxic fluorinated gases are produced. If these are inhaled through a lighted cigarette they beome more dangerous. Toxic products from decomposing fluorinated materials should not be inhaled.

3 Fire hazards of plastics

a. The evolution of large quantities of smoke

Any materials in which there is a considerable amount of aromatic (benzene ring) structures will tend to give fires having large quantities of smoke. In this class may be included polyurethanes, phenol-formaldehyde resins, polystyrene, fibre-glass polyesters, epoxide resins and polycarbonates. With polyurethanes very large quantities of smoke are evolved in a short time, due to rapid flame spread.

Although it is not an aromatic, pvc can produce considerable volumes of smoke in fires.

b. Production of burning tars or droplets

Most thermoplastics melt on heating and thus in a fire they may form burning droplets which could cause a further spread of fire. Although polyurethane foams are not technically thermoplastics, they give burning drops of tar in a fire. On the other hand pvc, which is a thermoplastic, does not give burning droplets, but merely forms a tarry coke-like product.

c. Exotherms

The polymerisation process may well be exothermic (i.e. gives out heat). This problem concerns plastics raw-material producers, but under these circumstances there is a high degree of control of the processes. The cross-linking or curing process of thermosetting materials is also often exothermic; for example, cases have been known of polyurethane foam blocks starting fires due to the fact that exothermic heat formed during the curing process cannot escape from the foam blocks. This is due to the blocks having a very low thermal conductivity.

d. Catalysts

Various types of catalyst are used in polymerisation processes and include acids, alkalis, complex organo-metallic compounds and organic peroxides. Acids and alkalis present well-known hazards. Organo-metallic catalysts may be in the form of a slurry in flammable solvents; organo-metal compounds, such as aluminium triethyl, react violently with water. Organic peroxides are widely used as catalysts for polymerisation and curing processes and these materials are oxidising agents and therefore present a considerable fire risk. Under some conditions such materials could be explosive.

e. Use of flammable solvents

Flammable solvents, such as acetone, methyl ethyl ketone, toluene, industrial alcohol and methyl alcohol are widely used as solvents in various processes and also as cleaning fluids.

f. Dusts

In certain processes, particularly the manufacture of moulding materials, finely divided plastic dusts will be produced, and these present a fire and explosion hazard (see the *Manual, Part 6C: Section 1, 'Fires in Dusts'*. Spray-drying can produce powdered polymers of very fine sub-division.

g. Self-extinguishing plastics

Many plastics are described as self-extinguishing. Some are naturally so, such as pvc and phenol-formaldehyde resins. Others may be rendered so by chemical changes in the polymer molecule or by special additives, e.g. certain types of polyester fibre-glass resin or polyurethane foam. The term self-extinguishing means that if an external source of heat, i.e. a flame, is removed, any fire it causes will go out. Although this is doubtless true, self-extinguishing materials, once ignited and surrounded by burning combustible materials may themselves burn. The term self-extinguishing must not be supposed to mean 'non-flammable'.

4 Dangers associated with monomers

Monomers by definition are reactive compounds capable of polymerisation. Some, like ethylene, do not polymerise very easily and need exactly the right conditions. Others may polymerise by accident, due to the presence of impurities or other causes, and when this happens a great deal of heat may be given out. As these materials are mostly poor conductors of heat, the heat cannot get away and a fire may result. In addition to this problem, many monomers are also flammable materials and some of them are toxic. Many fairly stable monomers could start to polymerise in a fire with the ensuing added hazard of the heat given out by the polymerisation reaction; this could lead to further fire or even explosion.

Some of the more notable monomers used in the plastics industry are detailed below, but the number of monomers is very large and ever increasing, so the list cannot be considered as exhaustive.

a. Acrylonitrile

This a colourless, partially water-soluble flammable liquid with a faint, pungent odour. It can polymerise with explosive violence when exposed to certain organic peroxides or concentrated caustic alkalis. Acrylonitrile is highly toxic and can be absorbed through the skin and also through leather. It is used as a starting material in the manufacture of ABS plastics and certain synthetic rubbers.

b. Butadiene

This a gas at room temperature and pressures, but it is easily liquefiable by moderate pressure at room temperature. It polymerises readily, especially in the presence of peroxide catalysts or air; in addition it is flammable. It is slightly toxic and narcotic in high concentration.

c. Epichlorhydrin

This is a monomer used in the manufacture of epoxy resins. It is a colourless, slightly water-soluble liquid with an irritating odour. It can polymerise exothermically with acids, bases and some salts. It is a highly toxic material and in fires may evolve toxic gases including phosgene.

d. Methyl methacrylate

A clear liquid with a rather acrid odour, which is used in the manufacture of acrylic plastics. It is flammable, somewhat toxic and can polymerise exothermically with peroxide catalysts. It is normally stabilised, but heat will accelerate the polymerisation process.

e. Styrene

This is used in the manufacture of polystyrene plastics and also in fibre-glass polyester resins. The material is a slightly yellow liquid having a strong characteristic smell. The tendency to polymerise, normally held in check by added inhibiters, is greatly accelerated by heat or added peroxides. This polymerisation is exothermic and fires and even explosions could occur under some circumstances. The material is moderately toxic and the vapour is an irritant to the eyes.

f. Vinyl acetate

This a colourless, slightly water-soluble, flammable liquid with a faint odour. It polymerises in contact with organic peroxides or when heated. It has a low order of toxicity, but may act as an eye irritant.

g. Vinyl chloride

At room temperatures and pressures, this material is a sweet-smelling gas which is easily liquefied by increased pressure. There is a severe explosion hazard when the material is exposed to heat or flame. It is moderately toxic and in high concentrations acts as an anaesthetic. The liquid may cause freeze burns due to rapid evaporation. The material is flammable and the combustion gases contain phosgene and hydrogen chloride and are thus toxic.

5 Intermediates and hardeners

a. Isocyanates

These are of several types and are used as intermediates in the manufacture of polyurethane foams. Most of them are brown liquids, slightly soluble in water and having a characteristic odour. They are skin irritants and may cause dermatitis and are toxic by skin absorption. They are flammable and emit toxic gases when on fire.

On breathing isocyanate vapours, bronchial spasm may be caused, and repeated exposure may bring about sensitisation. The exact toxic nature of these materials is a matter of controversy, but great caution should be exercised in dealing with them. They may be rendered harmless by special solutions of ammonia in water, to which an emulsifying agent has been added. In manufacture dangerous exothermic reaction causing fires can readily occur where toluene di-isocyanate (TDI) based foams are produced, but is much less likely where the more extensively used diphenyl methane di-isocyanate (MDI) foams are made.

b. Chlorosilanes

Again these are of several types, and they are intermediates in the manufacture of silicone plastics. Most are fuming clear liquids; they are highly toxic, flammable and react with water to produce hydrogen chloride gas. This reaction is strongly exothermic in many cases.

c. Epoxide resins

There are many different hardeners for these plastics. One class is known as amines, which may be either aliphatic or aromatic. In general these materials are more or less toxic and some of them may cause dermatitis.

Chapter 10
Other combustible solids

1 Wood

Wood is a complex polymeric material closely allied to cellulose. In spite of the wide use of synthetic materials, wood still accounts for a great deal of useful non-metallic material.

There is a high water content in wood and the wide difference in moisture content between green and well-dried wood is significant in regard to fire risk. Considerable quantities of heat are required to dry timber, due to the high latent heat of vaporisation of water. When wood is heated, a marked decomposition occurs at 170°C with the evolution of carbon dioxide, carbon monoxide and water due to the decomposition of the polymeric material of which wood is composed. At 302°C an exothermic reaction occurs, still further decomposing the wood. The liberation of heat can enable the late stages of carbonisation to occur without further external heating.

The properties of wood are such that a long-flaming fuel is produced, which burns readily and spreads fire quickly. Many methods have been used to try to render wood either non-flammable or less flammable. These methods depend usually on impregnating or painting the wood with suitable materials, of which there are many, such as borax, water-glass, sulphate, ammonium salts and other compounds sold under trade names.

2 Coal

Coal is formed by the action of pressure and temperature on the decayed vegetable products of ancient forests. Coal is a very complex mixture of carbon and a variety of resinous organic compounds. There are many varieties of coal and they may be roughly divided into hard and soft, the harder coals containing more carbon. The softer coals are more useful for gas-making and the harder coals for use in special furnaces for raising steam. Plates of inorganic, non-combustible materials are also found in coal, and these consist of limestone and compounds of iron, magnesium and manganese. The surface of coal has reactive centres where combination with oxygen can occur, and spontaneous ignition of coal is attributed to direct oxidation. It is clear that the smaller the coal particles, the greater the danger. It is promoted by moisture and the greater the oxygen content of the coal, the greater the danger, so that coal, especially pulverised coal containing more than 10 per cent of oxygen, may be dangerous in storage. In addition, a small proportion of the coal dust can form an explosive mixture in air. When the temperature is in excess of 60°C ignition may occur within a week or so. Storage heaps must be kept as free as possible from excess of air and external sources of heat should be avoided. Coal is sometimes sprayed with a high flash-point mineral oil that not only reduces dustiness, but also protects coal surfaces against oxidation.

The subject of fires in coal stacks is dealt with in the *Manual, Part 6C: Section 5, 'Fires in Fuels'*.

3 Metals

Three-quarters of all the elements are metals, though some of them are very rare. To a chemist a metal is a substance which can loose electrons and form positive ions (as already explained); ions are charged atoms or groups of atoms. In addition metals have a group of properties associated with them; if an element possesses most of them we describe it as a metal.

a. Properties of metals

(i)   All except mercury are solids.

(ii) They are malleable and ductile, i.e. they can be hammered into shape and drawn into wires.

(iii) They are good conductors of heat and electricity.

(iv) They have relatively high melting and boiling points.

(v)   They can form alloys.

(vi) Many of them combine with oxygen.

(vii) The oxides and hydroxides are basic.

(viii) They usually dissolve in mineral acids, often releasing hydrogen.

Metals show a wide range of chemical properties and range from dangerously reactive metals such as sodium to inert metals such as gold. Metals can be arranged in an 'Activity Series' (Table 11). In this Table, the most reactive metals are at the top and the least reactive at the bottom. Whatever chemical property is considered, those metals at the top of the series react most vigorously, indeed often violently, and those at the bottom react slowly or not at all. Although hydrogen is not a metal, it is included in the Table, as it also forms a positive ion. Many important metal reactions involve displacement of hydrogen either from water or from acids.

b. Reaction of metals with water or steam

(1) Potassium to calcium

These metals react immediately with water to release flammable hydrogen gas and leave a metal hydroxide. In some cases the hydroxide so formed is itself a corrosive alkali. In the case of potassium the reaction is so vigorous that the metal seems to ignite on contact with water. Sodium moves rapidly about on the surface of water and if prevented from doing so, it will ignite. Larger pieces of

Table 11

The activity series of metals

Metal		Occurrence	Reaction with water
Potassium	K	Never found uncombined	React with cold water to
Sodium	Na	with other elements	yield hydrogen
*Barium	Ba		
Strontium	Sr		
Calcium	Ca		
Magnesium	Mg	Rarely found	Burning metals
Aluminium	Al	uncombined with	decompose water and
*Chromium	Cr	other elements	hot metals decompose
Manganese	Mn		steam
Zince	Zn		
*Cadmium	Cd		
Iron	Fe		
Cobalt	Co		Very little reaction
Nickel	Ni		unless at white heat
Tin	Sn		
*Lead	Pb		
†HYDROGEN	H		
Bismuth	Bi	Sometimes found	Inactive with water or
Copper	Cu	uncombined with	steam
*Mercury	Hg	other elements	
Silver	Ag		
Platinum	Pt	Found uncombined	
Gold	Au	with other elements	

* Indicates that breathing apparatus should be worn in an incident involving these metals.

† Although not a metal, hydrogen is included as it also forms a positive ion.

these metals are in danger of explosion on contact with water. Calcium reacts steadily with cold water but vigorously with hot.

(2) Magnesium to iron

These metals show little reaction with cold water, even when magnesium is powdered. At higher temperatures, the reaction rate increases and a steady flow of hydrogen is produced by reaction with steam. If the metals are already burning the reaction with cold water becomes very high. Addition of cold water to burning magnesium gives rapid production of hydrogen with subsequent explosions. As the Activity Series scale is descended, the rate of reaction decreases until, with iron, there is little reaction unless the red-hot metal is treated with steam.

(3) Cobalt to lead

Here the white-hot metals must be treated with steam before reaction will take place.

(4) Bismuth to gold

Since these metals are below hydrogen in the Activity Series, there are no reactions with water or steam.

c. Formation of oxides and combustion

Metals at the top of the Activity Series react most readily with oxygen; sodium and potassium are so reactive that they are stored immersed in paraffin oil to prevent such oxidation. Many other metals will burn in air or oxygen, though with increasing difficulty as one descends the series. Even metals like tin and lead will burn at very high temperatures.

When the metal is very finely divided and so presents a greatly increased surface area, the ease of combustion may be vastly increased. Some metallic powders and dusts can burn or explode spontaneously in air. When this occurs at ordinary temperatures the material is said to be *pyrophoric*. The property of being pyrophoric is shared by many flammable metal powders and dusts, especially magnesium, calcium, sodium, potassium, zirconium, hafnium. Some metal powders have been known to burn in carbon dioxide, nitrogen or under water. Metal powders when damp may also cause fires and explosions, even in the absence of air and often without warning, and in the absence of heat.

The subject of metal fires, dusts and extinguishing methods is dealt with in detail in the *Manual, Part 6C*.

4 Sulphur

This is usually found either as a yellow powder (known as 'flowers of sulphur') or as yellow crystals, but it is sometimes produced as blocks or sticks. It burns with a blue flame to give sulphur dioxide:

$$S + O_2 = SO_2$$

Sulphur is used in the manufacture of rubber, in sulphur compounds, such as sulphur dioxide and sulphuric acid and in certain drugs. It has a low toxicity, but the dust presents an explosion hazard. Sulphur dioxide, however, is a highly toxic gas with a sharp pungent odour which can be easily liquefied under pressure at ambient temperatures. It has many uses, especially as a bleaching agent and as a food preservative.

Hydrogen sulphide (H_2S), which is also known as sulphuretted hydrogen, is formed as a by-product from many chemical processes, including the decomposition of organic sulphur compounds; for this reason it is frequently found in sewer gases. Hydrogen sulphide has a characteristic odour of rotten eggs and is highly toxic. It is flammable and under certain conditions can explode. (See also the *Manual, Part 6C: Section 16*).

5 Phosphorus

The element phosphorus is extremely reactive and is found in nature combined with other elements, mostly as phosphates (compounds containing the PO_4 group). It is also present in all living matter. The element exists in two different forms: red phosphorus and white (or yellow) phosphorus. Their properties are itemised in *Part 6C, Section 16*.

White phosphorus is extremely dangerous as it will ignite in air at temperatures as low as 30°C to give dense white clouds of toxic fumes of phosphorus pentoxide:

$$4P + 5O_2 \longrightarrow 2P_2O_5$$

White phosphorus should never be touched with the bare hands as their warmth may cause ignition; moreover phosphorus burns only heal very slowly.

Red phosphorus is relatively safe if handled with care, and is used in making safety matches. The white form, because of its toxicity, is converted to phosphorus sulphide (P_4S_3) for use in non-safety matches.

Inorganic metallic phosphates are crystalline solids which are normally safe unless one of the toxic metals is involved. Some of these metallic phosphates are used as fertilisers. Organic phosphates are often very toxic indeed and are found as pesticides; with some of these a few drops on the skin can prove fatal.

6 The halogens

Fluorine, chlorine, bromine and iodine are a group of elements known as halogens. They show a resemblance to each other, and the compounds formed also have somewhat similar properties. A summary of some of their properties is given in Table 12.

a. Fluorine

This is the most reactive non-metal known and reacts with most other elements. As a result, fluorine is usually found combined, as in such compounds as sodium fluoride (NaF). The gas is extremely toxic and dangerous because of its high reactivity with compounds that can be oxidised. It will react with water to produce great heat, giving off toxic and corrosive fumes. Fluorine is also found combined in organic compounds, such as the freons (used as refrigerant gases), certain anaesthetics, in the plastic ptfe (polytetrafluoroethylene) and in 'Viton' synthetic rubbers. On heating to decomposition, these materials give off various types of toxic gas.

Table 12

The Halogens

Property	Fluorine	Chlorine	Bromine	Iodine
Atomic weight	19	35·5	80	127
Physical state	Gas	Gas	Liquid	Solid
Colour	Pale yellow	Greenish yellow	Red	Grey-violet
Specific gravity	1·14 (liquid)	1·51 (liquid)	3·12 (liquid)	4·92 (solid)
Boiling point (°C)	−187	−34·6	58·9	184
Melting point (°C)	−223	−101	−7·2	114
Chemical activity	Extremely active	Very active	Less active	Least active
Oxidising power	Most powerful	Very powerful	Less powerful	Least powerful
Action with water	Decomposes it	Dissolves to form acid solution	Dissolves	Slightly soluble

b. Chlorine

This is the commonest, but most important of the halogens. It is easily liquefied under pressure at room temperature, the critical temperature being 144°C. Chlorine is an extemely toxic gas and was used as a poison gas in World War I. It reacts with water to form hydrochloric acid and hydrochlorous acid:

$$H_2O + Cl_2 = HCl + HClO$$

Chlorine is a highly reactive element and an oxidising agent; it can react, and even cause explosions, with turpentine, ether, ammonia gas, hydrocarbons, hydrogen and powdered metals. The reaction with acetylene is especially violent and noteworthy. Large quantities of chlorine are used in the bleaching wood pulp, cotton and linen fabrics; also in the manufacture of chlorine compounds, such as carbon tetrachloride (CTC), hydrochloric acid, chlorates, chlorinated plastics and insecticides. (See also *Part 6C: Section 16*).

c. Bromine

At room temperature bromine is a dark red liquid which readily releases toxic vapours. The liquid causes serious burns if it comes into contact with the skin. Bromine is an oxidising agent and may ignite combustible substances with which it comes into contact. It is used mainly to produce compounds; such as ethylene dibromide ($C_2H_4Br_2$), and salts, such as sodium bromide (NaBr). Bromine compounds are used in the manufacture of self-extinguishing plastics. (See also *Part 6C: Section 16*).

d. Iodine

This is a dark-violet, almost black, solid which sublimes readily to give off a violet toxic vapour. To some extent it can react with oxidisable materials. It is almost insoluble in water, but dissolves in alcohol to give tincture of iodine, which is sometimes used as an antiseptic.

Part 3
Extinguishing fire

In the previous Part the chemical reactions which produce fire were described from the scientific viewpoint. In this Part, it is now proposed to relate this knowledge to the subject of fire extinction, and to refer to the various methods at present employed.

Chapter 11
Methods of extinguishing fire

It has been shown from the *triangle of combustion* (see Fig. 6.1), that three factors are essential to combustion, namely:

(i) the presence of a fuel, or combustible substance;

(ii) the presence of oxygen (usually as air) or other supporter of combustion;

(iii) the attainment and maintenance of a certain minimum temperature.

Fire extinction, in principle, consists in the limitation of one or more of these factors, and the methods of extinguishing fire may therefore be classified conveniently under the following headings:

(1) Starvation

or the limitation of fuel.

(2) Smothering

or the limitation of oxygen.

(3) Cooling

or the limitation of temperature.

In practice, specific methods of fire extinction often embody more than one of these principles, but it will be convenient to consider them according to the main principle involved.

1 Starvation

The extinction of fire by starvation (Fig.11.1, *top*), is applied in three ways:

(i) By removing combustible material from the neighbourhood of the fire. Examples of this are, the drainage of fuel from burning oil tanks; the working out of cargo at a ship fire; the cutting of trenches in peat, heath and forest fires; the demolition of buildings to create a fire stop; counter-burning in forest fires.

(ii) By removing the fire from the neighbourhood of combustible material as, for instance, pulling apart a burning haystack or a thatched roof.

(iii) By sub-dividing the burning material, when the smaller fires produced may be left to burn out or to be extinguished more easily by other means. A typical example is the emulsification of the surface of burning oil, whilst the beating out of a heath fire owes much of its effectiveness to this.

(2) Smothering

If the oxygen content of the atmosphere in the immediate neighbour-hood of burning material can be sufficiently reduced combustion will cease (Fig. 11.1, *centre*). The general procedure in methods of this type is to prevent or impede the access of fresh air to the seat of the fire, and allow the combustion to reduce the oxygen content in the confined atmosphere until it extinguishes itself. This principle is, of course, ineffective where, as in the case of celluloid, the burning material contains within itself, in a chemically combined form, the oxygen it requires for combustion.

The principle of smothering is employed on a small scale in snuffing a candle, and, on a large scale, in capping a burning oil well: two processes which are precisely analogous. The battening down of a ship's hold when a fire breaks out below decks will often hold the flames in check until port is reached. Small fires, such as those involving a person's clothing, can be smothered with a rug, blanket, etc. while the use of sand or earth on a small metal fire is a further instance of the same principle.

An important practical application of the smothering method is the use of foam. This forms a viscous coating over the burning material and limits, in so far as it is complete, the supply of air. It also tends to prevent the formation of flammable vapour.

Another method of smothering is by the application of a cloud of finely divided particles of dry powder, usully sodium bicarbonate, from a pressurised extinguisher. Research has been made into this method and it is not certain that the action is solely related to smothering. Carbonates will absorb heat and when they are finely divided, as is the powder, their specific heat is very much greater. It may, therefore, be more accurate to say that the powder has a cooling effect in addition to its smothering effect.

A further development in the smothering method has been the discovery of a powdered compound for use on metal fires, such as uranium and plutonium, thorium and magnesium. This powder (ternary eutectic chloride) is applied by means of a gas cartridge pres-surised extinguisher. As the fusing temperature of the powder is in the region of 580°C, it is intended that it shall form a crust over the burning metal and thus exclude the oxygen of the air.

Another class of smothering agent may be described as temporary in its blanketing effect. Thus the vigorous discharge of an inert gas in

Fig. 11.1 The triangle of combustion. Top: starvation – or the limitation of the combustible material. Centre: smothering – or the limitation of oxygen. Bottom: cooling – or the limitation of temperature.

the immediate vicinity of the fire may so reduce the oxygen content of the atmosphere for the time being that combustion cannot be maintained. Carbon dioxide and nitrogen are familiar examples of this. With fires of any magnitude, however, the convection currents set up are sufficiently powerful to dissipate the inert atmosphere formed by the application of the gas blanket before the extinguishing action can take effect. The same thing happens if this method is used out of doors with a strong wind blowing. The application of these media in liquid form, which is then vaporised by the fire thus forming the required inert atmosphere, is more likely to be effective, particularly as a cooling effect is also operative (see Section 3 'Cooling').

Experiments over recent years have produced a group of extinguishants consisting of volatile liquids based on the *halogenated hydrocarbons*. The first and probably the simplest of these was *carbon tetrachloride*, but owing to its toxic effects, its use has been discontinued and a number of others of lesser toxicity have found favour. The best known in this county is *bromochlorodifluoromethane* (known as BCF), but a number of closely related compounds are used here and overseas. It would appear that these vaporising liquids act partly as inerting blankets similar to those mentioned in the preceding section and partly by chemical interference with the chain reaction of flame propagation. The more rapid the decomposition of the gas the faster is the reaction with the flame molecules and the sooner the extinguishment of the fire. This could account for the difference in the so-called '*inhibitory factors*' of this type of extinguishant.

One other method of fire extinction is the separation of the fuel from the flame by blasting it away. On a small scale the blowing out of a candle is an obvious example, while on the larger scale the extinguishing of an oil well fire by the blast from exploding dynamite is a practical use of the method. Such a technique does, of course, also involve to a considerable extent the cooling principle treated in the next section.

(1) Cooling

If the rate at which heat is generated by combustion is less than the rate at which it is dissipated through various agencies, the combustion cannot persist (Fig. 11.1, *bottom*). In applying this principle of fire extinction, the first step is to accelerate the speed with which heat is removed from the fire, thus reducing the temperature of the burning mass and as a consequence the rate at which heat is produced. In due course the rate at which heat is lost from the fire exceeds the rate of heat production and the fire dies away.

The application of a jet or spray of water to a fire is invariably based on this simple but fundamental principle. There are many variations: another example is the emulsification of the surface of oil by means of the emulsifying type of sprinkler head producing an oil-in-water or water-in-oil emulsion.

The cooling principle in fire extinction is the one most commonly employed, forming as it does the basis of the application of water and other liquids to burning materials. The extingushing medium operates by absorbing heat from the fire, as a consequence of which it may undergo one or more of the following changes:

(a) its temperature is raised;

(b) it is converted to the vapour state;

(c) it is decomposed;

(d) it reacts chemically with the burning material.

It is clearly desirable that the quantity of heat required to produce any or all of these changes in a given quantity of an extinguishing medium should be as high as possible. That is to say, referring specifically to the above headings, that the following values should be as high as possible:

(i)   the amount of heat absorbed for any given increase in temperature (the thermal capacity);

(ii) the amount of heat required to vaporise a unit weight of the extinguishing medium (the latent heat of vaporisation);

(iii) the amount of heat required to cause decomposition of a unit weight of the extinguishing medium (the heat of decomposition);

(iv) the amount of heat required to cause a unit weight of the extinguishing medium to react chemically with the burning material (the heat of reaction).

The action of water depends predominantly on (i) and (ii), the latter being by far the more important. Thus it takes about six times as much heat to convert a certain weight of water at its boiling point into steam as is required to raise the temperature of the same amount of water from the usual atmospheric value to its boiling point. In the interest of efficiency, then, it is clearly desirable that water should be applied to a fire in the liquid condition and in such a way that as much as possible is converted to steam. The smothering effect of the steam produced at the seat of the fire is thought to play a part in assisting in the extinguishing process. In all fire-fighting operations where water is in use it should be the aim to ensure that the proportion of water which escapes from the building in liquid form to that which is applied should be as low as possible. When the heat of a fire is considerable, as in its early stages, the steam formed will not be visible, but as the temperature falls the steam will condense above the fire. This is widely recognised by experienced fire officers as a sign that a fire is being brought under control.

On a basis of thermal capacity and latent heat of vaporisation, water is an excellent fire extinguisher, since both figures are high. This fact, combined with its availablity in large quantities, make it by far the most useful fire extinguisher for general purposes. The principle of decomposition probably has little application, as water is fairly stable except at very high temperatures. Certain substances, for example carbonates, absorb heat in this way (see the reference to dry powder extinguishers under Section 2, 'Smothering'). Water is not usually effective in absorbing much heat by reacting with the burning substance. Some extinguishing media may in certain circumstances prove dangerous in this connection, their reaction with the burning substance resulting in the evolution rather than the absorption of heat. Moreover, the reaction may result in the production of a substance which is itself combustible, thus adding fuel to the fire. The action of water on burning magnesium exemplifies both these effects, since it reacts with the metal exothermically (i.e. producing heat) with the formation of hydrogen, which is readily ignited. In the case of other media the reaction products may be undesirable in other senses, as in the case of carbon tetrachloride which, under certain conditions, may evolve phosgene, a hight poisonous gas.

Chapter 12
Fire extinguishing media

The principles underlying the methods employed in extinguishing fire have been dealt with in the previous chapters. Here it is proposed to show the various media which are used for particular types of fire. These will depend upon the nature of the materials involved and the size and intensity of the fire.

1 Classification of fires by type

In the United Kingdom, fires in the past have been unofficially classified into four types, namely A, B, C and M denoting respectively carbonaceous fires, flammable liquids fires, electrical fires and metal fires. Agreement has now been reached between European nations on a new classification which forms the subject of British Standard BS–EN 2: 1972 (formerly BS 4547: 1970) entitled 'Classification of Fires', as follows:

Class 'A'

These are fires involving solid materials normally of an organic nature (compounds of carbon), in which combustion generally occurs with the formation of glowing embers. Class 'A' fires are the most common and the most effective extinguishing agent is generally water in the form of a jet or spray.

Class 'B'

These are fires involving liquids or liquefiable solids. For the purpose of choosing effective extinguishing agents, flammable liquids may be divided into two groups:

    (i)   those that are miscible with water,

         and

    (ii) those that are immiscible with water.

Depending on (i) and (ii), the extinguishing agents include water spray, foam, light water, vaporising liquids, carbon dioxide and dry chemical powders.

Class 'C'

These are fires involving gases or liquefied gases in the form of a liquid spillage, or a liquid or gas leak, and these include methane, propane, butane, etc. Foam or dry chemical powder can be used to control fires involving shallow liquid spills. (Water in the form of spray is generally used to cool the containers.)

Class 'D'

These are fires involving metals. Extinguishing agents containing water are ineffective, and even dangerous; carbon dioxide and the bicarbonate classes of dry chemical powders may also be hazardous if applied to most metal fires. Powdered graphite, powdered talc, soda ash, limestone and dry sand are normally suitable for Class 'D' fires. Special fusing powders have been developed for fires involving some metals, especially the radioactive ones.

Electrical fires

It is not considered, according to present-day ideas, that electrical fires constitute a class, since any fire involving, or started by, electrical equipment must, in fact, be a fire of Class A, B or D. The normal procedure in such circumstances is to cut off the electricity and use an extinguishing method appropriate to what is burning. Only when this cannot be done with certainty will special extinguishing agents be required which are non-conductors of electricity and non-damaging to equipment; these include vaporising liquids, dry powders and carbon dioxide, although the latter's cooling and condensation effects may affect sensitive electronic equipment.

2 Classification of fires by size

To describe the size of a fire, the Central Fire Brigades Advisory Council has made the following recommendation:

Major Fire	20+ jets
Large fire	8–19 jets
Medium fire	3–7 jets
Small fire	1–2 jets, or 3+ hose reels
Minor fire	1–2 hose reels, or hand extinguishers.

3 Water

Despite the many new techniques which have come to the assistance of firemen, water is still the most efficient, cheapest and most readily available medium for extinguishing fires of a general nature. It is used by fire brigades for the majority of fires, although the methods of application have undergone a number of improvements. If more water is applied than is actually required to contain and extinguish the fire, the surplus will drain off, or will seep through floors and perhaps cause more damage to goods and property than that caused by the fire itself. Accordingly, the method of applying water to a fire varies according to the size of the fire.

If small quantities only are required, the necessary force may be obtained by the use of portable extinguishers expelling water, or by the use of hand pumps. Where the fire is larger than can be dealt with by hand appliances, then hose reels are used instead. The water for these is contained in a tank incorporated on the appliance and is pumped through the tubing on the reels by means of a built-in pump. For major fires, greater quantities of water are necessary, and the built-in pumps driven by the vehicles' engines are often capable of pumping up to 4500 litres per minute, giving the necessary energy to the water to provide adequate striking power.

A variation in the application of water can be made by means of nozzles that produce jets or sprays ranging from large size droplets down to atomised fog effects. Judicious use of this type of application can not only cut down the amount of water used, minimising water damage, but will ensure that it is used to greater effect. Atomised spray (fog) nozzles have become standard equipment on fire brigade appliances in this county, particularly the low pressure types that can be operated from hose reels. They are quite effective when used in the correct situations, but their range is limited. Special pumps and ancillary equipment are used with high pressure fog, giving a greater range of application, but the special equipment makes it a less economical proposition.

4 Steam

Steam in large quantities can be used to smother a fire and in situations where it is readily available, it can be used in fixed installations. Compartmentation is obviously a help and ships are frequently adapted to be able to fill holds with steam under pressure.

5 Foam and foam-making compounds

Some of the most hazardous substances so far as fire risk is concerned, are liquids having a specific gravity lower than that of water. When water is applied to the burning surface of such a liquid, it lowers the temperature momentarily and then sinks below the surface where any further effect is lost, except in the case of liquids such as methylated spirits which mix freely with water, and where dilution may therefore occur to the point where combustion cannot be maintained.

It was shown in Chapter 11 that one of the methods which can be employed for fire extinction is smothering, or the limitation of oxygen. Foam, which is relatively insoluble in most liquids and because of its light weight floats on the surface of the liquid, forms a blanket capable of covering the surface of the burning liquid and so extinguishes the fire. It also forms a radiant heat barrier which is of importance in the extinction of oil and petrol fires.

Foam as used by fire brigades is usually generated by the mechanical agitation of a diluted foam compound solution in the presence of air. These compounds include soaps, glue and wetting agent mixtures and hydrolised protein concentrates. This type of foam compound produces foam with the most suitable characteristics for general use by fire brigades for fighting large fires in oil and petrol tanks, and is the standard compound used in this county. It is manufactured by the acid or alkaline hydrolysis of hoof and horn meal or animal blood.

The desirable characteristics of foam are resistance to radiant heat, to fuel vapours and to loss of water content by drainage. It should flow readily and recover a surface if disturbed, without being too sloppy. The most satisfactory measure of the efficiency of the foam as a fire-fighting agent is the minimum rate of application at which a fire is controlled by the agent. It is usual to allow 50 litres per square metre of surface area per minute as the ideal rate, although in most cases it would be rather less than this.

Normal protein foam is destroyed rapidly by polar solvents such as alcohols and ketones and because of this, application rates have to be very high, up to five times the normal. Some work has been done on alcohol resistant and all-purpose foams, but there are disadvantages yet to be overcome. Another line of research has produced what is sometimes known as 'light water' which holds promise for the future. The so-called 'light water' is a perfluorinated hydrocarbon dissolved in water. This makes a foam which is much less viscous than is usual without losing its inherent strength, and so it flows rapidly over the surface producing a sealing effect. When the surface is disturbed and flashback occurs, the re-sealing is extremely fast. It is generally intended to be used in combination with dry powder, particularly the potassium-based powder known as 'Purple K'. This combination produces the quick knock-down associated with dry powder application, while the light water produces the sealing effect necessary to consolidate the complete extinction without re-ignition.

Another variety of foam is known as 'high expansion foam' which has an expansion ratio of up to 1000 to 1 instead of about 8 to 1 for standard foam. High expansion foam has a particular application for dealing with carbonaceous fires in compartments which are inaccessible and which lend themselves to complete flooding of the compartment.

6 Vaporising liquids

The halogenated hydrocarbons used for extinguishing fires have the property of vaporising readily when heated and are, therefore, generally known as vaporising liquids. They form a dense, heavier-than-air, cloud of non-flammable vapour which not only blankets a fire by the displacement of air, but also has the property of interfering with the chemical reaction of flame propagation in the burning material.

Vaporising liquids have an especial use for extinguishing fires involving electrical equipment, as they are non-conductors of electricity and they are also non-injurious to delicate electronic equipment. Vaporising liquid extinguishers are also excellent for dealing with fires involving laboratory equipment, or for extinguishing fires in the engines of motor vehicles. Their greatest drawback has been their toxicity and this has led to the recommended withdrawal of some well-known extinguishing media from the group, namely carbon tetrachloride and methyl bromide. This has left the field open to the 'freon' types which, because of the introduction of fluorine to the mixtures, tend to be less toxic. The most common substances used are chlorobromomethane (CBM), bromochlorodifluoromethane (BCF) and bromotrifluoromethane (BTM).

7 Carbon dioxide and inert gases

At normal temperatures, carbon dioxide is a gas $1 \cdot 5$ times as dense as air. It is easily liquefied and bottled, where it is contained under a pressure of approximately 50 bar. As a fire extinguishant it acts in a similar manner to vaporising liquids, and when a CO_2 extinguisher is discharged, the liquid boils off rapidly as a gas, extracting heat from the surrounding atmosphere. The gas, however, extinguishes by smothering, or reducing the oxygen content of the air and about 20 to 30 per cent is necessary to completely extinguish, according to the nature of the burning material; in fact, materials which supply their own oxygen will continue to burn, as will any material that tends to decompose the carbon dioxide, such as burning magnesium. Apart from these considerations, carbon dioxide is quick and clean, non-conductive of electricity, non-toxic and does not harm most fabrics.

For fire situations, such as in transformer chambers, where complete flooding of the compartment is desirable, fixed carbon dioxide installations may be built in. Carbon dioxide is also available in bulk to fire authorities, by special arrangement with certain manufacturers who have agreed to supply tankers containing 10 tonne of liquid to any fire on request.

As an alternative to carbon dioxide, liquid nitrogen in bulk or in cylinders containing the gas will also produce the inerting or smothering effect necessary for successful extinction. Several inert gas systems using combustible products of diesel oil have also been developed, and these may sometimes be found installed to flood cargo holds or tanks on board ships. Research is being pursued to determine the value of inert gas produced from mobile generators for all types of fire, but this work is still in an experimental stage.

8 Dry chemical powders

New problems have been produced for the fireman by the use in industry of an ever widening range of materials. Plastics is one example of this, and the fabrication of titanium, zirconium, beryllium and other metals is another. Water can often not be used; on most fires involving burning metals, the result of applying water can be explosively disastrous, and so new methods of extinction have been evolved. Chief among these are powdered chemicals which are stored in cylinders under pressure, or which can be ejected by the release of gas under pressure.

The basis of most chemical powders is sodium bicarbonate. This, with the addition of a metallic stearate as a waterproofing agent, is widely used as an extinguishant, not only in portable extinguishers, but also for general application in large quantities. Apart from stearates, other additives are sometimes used to decrease the bulk density and to reduce packing in the cylinder.

Dry chemical is expelled from containers by gas pressure and, by means of specially designed nozzles, is directed at the fire in a concentrated cloud. This cloud also screens the operator from the flames and enables a relatively close attack to be made. Dry chemical powder can also be supplied in polythene bags for metal fires, as it is more effective to bury the fire under a pile of bags which melt and allow the contents to smother the fire.

Special powders have been developed for some metal fires, especially for the radioactive metals such as uranium and plutonium. These are known as the ternary eutectic chloride group and were researched and perfected by the United Kingdom Atomic Energy Authority. These powders contain an ingredient which melts, then flows a little and forms a crust over the burning metal, effectively sealing it from the surrounding atmosphere and isolating the fire. Dry chemical powders are also tested for their compatibility with foam, as it was discovered that the early powders tended to break down foam, and the two should complement each other on fires where foam is the standard extinguishant.

9 Sand, etc.

Some burning materials, such as metals, which cannot be extinguished by the use of water, may be dealt with by means of dry

earth, dry sand, powdered graphite, powdered talc, soda ash or limestone, all of which act as a smothering agent. Dry sand may also be
used to prevent burning liquids, such as paints and oils, from flowing
down drains, basement lights, etc. and for confining shallow layers of
such liquids, thus permitting the use of foam or spray branches. On
no account should sand be used for extinguishing fires in machinery,
such as electric motors, since its use may well necessitate dismantling
the entire machine for cleaning, even though the fire damage is
negligible.

10 Blanketing

Another method by which fire may be extinguished, especially for
persons whose clothing is on fire, is by blanketing. The person should
be laid down and covered or rolled in a rug, coat, jacket, woollen
blanket, etc. For dealing with fires in small utensils, such as those
containing cooking fats, the best method is to smother the fire with an
asbestos blanket, or similar material, such as a doormat which has
been wetted first.

11 Beating out

Small fires in materials, such as textiles, etc. may often be
extinguished by beating them out, or by rolling and screwing up the
burning material tightly to exclude the air. Beating is also the method
normally employed to extinguish heath, crop and other similar fires
in rural areas when water is not readily available.

Structure and publishing history of the
Manual of firemanship

The *Manual of Firemanship* was first published in a series of nine 'Parts' (1–5, 6a, 6b, 6c and 7) between 1943 and 1962.

In July 1974, it was decided that these nine Parts should be gradually replaced by 18 'Books' and a revised format for the *Manual* was drawn up. The new Books were to up-date the information given and arrange the subjects covered in more compact and coherent groups, each group occupying one of the new Books. The following pages show the original plan, *as amended to date.* Book 4 is the twelfth of these Books to be published.

Since 1974 there have been many developments in Fire Brigade practice and equipment and in the problems which firemen may have to face. To remain an authoritative and up-to-date survey of the science of firefighting the *Manual* must take these developments into account. Not all the necessary changes can be accommodated within the format announced in 1974. The reader should therefore be aware that the structure of unpublished Books of the *Manual*, as set out on the following pages is subject to change. Such changes will be publicised as far in advance as possible.

The next Book planned for publication is the revision of Book 7 including a section on "Pumps, primers and pump operation".

Manual of Firemanship

Book 1 Elements of combustion and
extinction (published in 1974)

Part	*Formerly*	
	Part	*Chapter*
1 Physics of combustion	*1*	*1*
2 Chemistry of combustion	*1*	*1*
3 Methods of extinguishing fire	*1 and*	*2*
	6a	*32 (III)*

Book 2 Fire Brigade equipment (published
in 1974)

Part	*Formerly*	
	Part	*Chapter*
1 Hose	*1*	*4*
2 Hose fittings	*1*	*5*
3 Ropes and lines, knots, slings, etc.	*1 and*	*7*
	6a	*39*
4 Small gear	*1*	*13*

Book 3 Fire extinguishing equipment
(published in 1976)

Part	*Formerly*	
	Part	*Chapter*
1 Hand and stirrup pumps	*1*	*8*
2 Portable chemical extinguishers	*1*	*9*
3 Foam and foam making equipment	*1*	*10*

Book 4 Incidents involving aircraft, shipping
and trains (published 1985)

Part	*Information available in*		
	Part	*Chapter*	*Last edition*
1 Incidents involving aircraft	*6b*	*4*	*1973*
2 Incidents involving shipping	*7*	*1–3*	*1972*
3 Incidents involving trains	*6b*	*3*	*1973*

Book 5 Ladders and appliances (published in 1984)

Part	*Formerly*	
	Part	*Chapter*
1 Extension ladders, hook ladders and roof ladders	*1*	*6*
2 Escapes	*2*	*3*
3 Turntable ladders	*2*	*4*
4 Hydraulic platforms	*2*	*5*
5 Special appliances	*2*	*6*
6 Pumping appliances	*2*	*1*

Book 6 Breathing apparatus and resuscitation
  (published in 1974)

Part	Formerly Part	Chapter
1 Breathing apparatus	1	11
2 Operational procedure	6a	32(V)
3 Resuscitation	1	12

Book 7 (first edition) Hydraulics and water
  supplies (published in 1975)

Part	Formerly Part	Chapter
1 Hydraulics	3	19
2 Hydrants and water supplies	3	20
3 Water relaying	3	21
Appendices		

Book 7 (second edition) (not yet published)

As above, plus

	Information available in	
4 Pumps, primers and pump operation	2	1–2

Book 8 Building construction and structural fire
  protection (published in 1975)

Part	Formerly Part	Chapter
1 Materials	4	23
2 Elements of structure	4	23
3 Building design	4	23

Book 9 Fire protection of buildings (published
  in 1977)

Part	Formerly Part	Chapter
1 Fire extinguishing systems	4	24/26
2 Fire alarm systems	5	28
3 Fire venting systems	4	23

Book 10 Fire Brigade communications (published
  in 1978)

Part	Formerly Part	Chapter
1 The public telephone system and its relationship to the Fire Service	5	27
2 Mobilising arrangements	5	29
3 Call-out and remote control systems	5	30
4 Radio	5	31
5 Automatic fire alarm signalling systems	5	28

Book 11 Practical firemanship (published
  in 1981)

Part	Formerly Part	Chapter
1 Practical firefighting	6a	32
2 Methods of entry into buildings	6a	35
3 Control at a fire	6a	33

Book 12 Practical firemanship (published in 1983)

Part	Formerly	
	Part	Chapter
1 Fire Service rescues	6a	36
2 Decontamination	–	–
3 Ventilation at fires	6a	37
4 Salvage	6a	38
5 After the incident	6a	34

Book 13
Contents not yet decided

Book 14 Special fires I (not yet published)

Part	Information available in		
	Part	Chapter	Last edition
1 Fires in animal and vegetable oils	6c	45(8)	1970
2 Fires in fats and waxes	6c	45(3)	1970
3 Fires in resins and gums	6c	45(13)	1970
4 Fires in grain, hops, etc.	6c	45(6)	1970
5 Fires in fibrous materials	6c	45(4)	1970
6 Fires in sugar	6c	45(15)	1970
7 Fires in paint and varnishes	6c	45(9)	1970

Book 15 Special fires II (not yet published)

Part	Information available in		
	Part	Chapter	Last edition
1 Fires in dusts	6c	45(1)	1970
2 Fires in explosives	6c	45(2)	1970
3 Fires in metals	6c	45(7)	1970
4 Fires in plastics	6c	45(10)	1970
5 Fires in involving radioactive materials	6c and	45(11)	1970
	6a	33(VI)	1971
6 Fires in refrigeration plant	6c	45(12)	1970
7 Fires in rubber	6c	45(14)	1970

Book 16 Special fires III (not yet published)

Part	Information available in		
	Part	Chapter	Last edition
1 Fires in rural areas	6b	1	1973
2 Fires in electricity undertakings	6b	3	1973

Book 17 Special fires IV (not yet published)

Part	Information available in		
	Part	Chapter	Last edition
1 Fires in fuels	6c	45(5)	1970
2 Fires in oil refineries	6b	5	1973
3 Fires in gas works	6b	2	1973

Book 18 Contents not yet decided.

Printed for Her Majesty's Stationery Office
by Robendene Ltd., Amersham.
Dd 739337 C60 4/86

NOTES

NOTES

NOTES